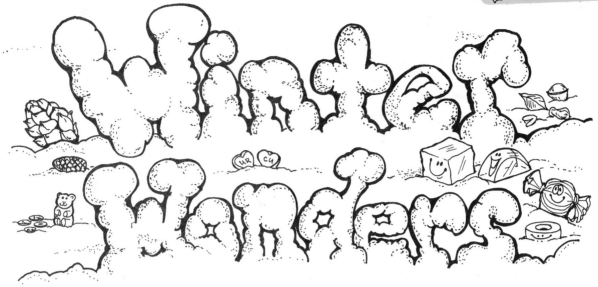

Principal Authors
Carol Gossett
Evalyn Hoover

Contributing Authors
Betty Cordel
Suzy Gazlay
Elaine Haven
Nicki Klevan
Sheryl Mercier
Barbara Novelli
1997 AIMS Leadership Primary Group

Desktop Publishing
Tanya Adams

Illustrator
Sheryl Mercier

Editor
Betty Cordel

WINTER WONDERS

© 2001 AIMS Education Foundation

This book contains materials developed by the AIMS Education Foundation. **AIMS** (**A**ctivities **I**ntegrating **M**athematics and **S**cience) began in 1981 with a grant from the National Science Foundation. The non-profit AIMS Education Foundation publishes hands-on instructional materials (books and the monthly magazine) that integrate curricular disciplines such as mathematics, science, language arts, and social studies. The Foundation sponsors a national program of professional development through which educators may gain both an understanding of the AIMS philosophy and expertise in teaching by integrated, hands-on methods.

ISBN 1-881431-94-0

Printed in the United States of America

I Hear and I Forget,

I See and I Remember,

I Do and I Understand.

—Chinese Proverb

Table of Contents

Secrets in the Bag

Topic
Observation

Key Question
How do our senses help us learn information about objects?

Focus
The students will increase their observational skills.

Guiding Documents
Project 2061 Benchmark
• *People use their senses to find out about their surroundings and themselves. Different senses give different information. Sometimes a person can get different information about the same thing by moving closer to it or further away from it.*

NRC Standard
• *Describing things as accurately as possible is important in science because it enables people to compare their observations with those of others.*

Science
Life science
    human senses

Integrated Processes
Observing
Recording
Comparing and contrasting
Communicating
Predicting

Materials
For each student:
    a decorated bag (see *Management 1*)

For each pair of students:
    a pre-packed paper bag *(see Management 2)*
    several holiday related objects (see *Management 2*)
    Sense Cards

For the class:
    chart paper

Background Information
Observation is the most basic of skills. Observations are made using any or all of our five senses—sight, smell, taste, hearing, and touch. It is the foundation of all other skills. Students need it to compare and contrast objects, sort and classify, measure, and predict. It is essential that students be taught the skill of observation while involved in experiences that are child-centered and have real-world applications.

Young learners also need to develop skills of communication in order to tell others what they observe and what they think. They need to be able to compare their observations with those of others.

This activity combines the use of senses to make observations and to practice communication.

Management
1. Each student will need a small paper bag. You may want them to decorate the bags prior to the lesson to keep with a holiday theme.
2. Each pair of students will need a pre-packed paper bag that is prepared by the teacher. Place three or four holiday-related objects in the bag. For example: a bell, a small pine bough, a cinnamon stick, a holiday bow, peppermint candy cane, etc.
3. For each pair of students, copy, cut apart, and laminate for extended use, one set of the *Sense Cards*. NOTE: A taste *Sense Card* has been included; however, you will need to explain to the students that they must follow these rules: they are not allowed to taste anything until they have asked permission, nor are they allowed to taste anything that is not considered food.

Procedure
1. Divide the class into partners and give each child a paper bag. Give a pre-packed bag and a set of *Sense Cards* to each pair of students.
2. Direct one of the partners, without looking, to take one item from the pre-packed bag and to secretly place it into their partner's bag.
3. Tell the other partners to arrange the *Sense Cards*, face up, in front of them with the *sight* and *taste* cards last. Tell them that they may use the senses in any order they choose, except for the senses of sight and taste. They must save those senses for last.

4. Direct the students to point to the first card and to use the sense pictured on that card to explore what is in their bag. Ask them to name the sense they are using, to describe what they find out about the object using this sense, and to predict what the object may be. Then tell them to identify the next sense they will use. For example, I used my sense of hearing and I can observe that the object makes a ringing sound. This is a holiday bell, but I'm not sure what shape it is. I'm going to use my sense of touch to find out more about the object.

5. Encourage the students to feel the object, predict; smell the object, predict; listen to the object, predict; and finally, look at and taste the object, if appropriate, and tell what the object is. Emphasize that they have permission to taste only the objects that are considered food for humans.

6. Using a set of *Sense Cards*, place them on top of the five pieces of chart paper. As the students describe their observations and make predictions, record them on the appropriate charts. For example: It feels prickly, I think it might be _____. It smells like the forest, it might be _____. It smells good, I think it's a _____. It doesn't make a sound. It looks like a pine tree!

7. Taking turns, continue this process with all the items in the pre-packed bags.

Discussion

1. When you observe something, what are some things you can use to learn more about it? [my senses, tools]
2. Using our charts, what information did we gather about the thing in the bags using our sense of sight? ...touch? ...smell? ...hearing? ...taste?
3. Which of your senses do you think gives you the most information? Explain why you think this sense gives you the most information.
4. How would you observe something if you could not see? ...could not hear? ...could not taste?
5. What sense did you enjoy using the most?

Extension

Ask the students to pre-pack new bags and to exchange bags with other groups and repeat the activity.

Sense Cards

Surprise Bag

Ears

Hearing

Nose

Smelling

Tongue

Tasting

Eyes

Seeing

Skin

Touching

Sweet Sensations

Topic
Observation

Key Question
How do science tools help us gather information?

Focus
Using math and science tools, the students will use their observational skills and practice communication skills.

Guiding Documents
Project 2061 Benchmark
- *Tools such as thermometers, magnifiers, rulers, or balances often give more information about things than can be obtained by just observing things without their help.*

NRC Standards
- *Describing things as accurately as possible is important in science because it enables people to compare their observations with those of others.*
- *Objects have many observable properties, including size, weight, shape, color, temperature, and the ability to react with other substances. Those properties can be measured using tools, such as rulers, balances, and thermometers.*

NCTM Standards 2000*
- *Select an appropriate unit and tool for the attribute being measured*
- *Use tools to measure*

Math
Measurement

Science
Life science
human senses

Integrated Processes
Observing
Collecting and recording data
Sorting
Comparing and contrasting
Communicating
Applying

Materials
For each group of students:
  Sweet Sensations Measuring Tapes (see *Management 1*)
  hand lens
  microscope, optional
  one paper bag wrapped candy (see *Management 3*)
  scissors
  glue

For the class:
  chart paper

For each student:
  family note

Background Information
Students need to be taught the skill of observation as it is the foundation of science. In math and science, observation is used in many ways such as: comparing and contrasting, sorting and classifying, measuring and predicting.

Primary students need to develop the art of communication so they can tell others what they observe and what they think. By communicating, they can compare their observations, show what they know, and learn from others.

This activity combines the use of the senses in making observations and the practice of communication. The students also discover that by using math/science tools, their observations are enhanced.

Management
1. Prior to this lesson, duplicate and send home the family note asking for a variety of wrapped candy.
2. Duplicate a minimum of eight *Sweet Sensations Measuring Tapes* for each pair of students. Cutting the measuring tapes can prove to be difficult for students, so you may want to pre-cut them.
3. For each pair of students, gather two matching sets of wrapped candy (eight pieces in all). A set includes a variety of four pieces of candy and another set of four additional identical pieces. Place one set in a paper lunch bag and the matching set in a plastic sandwich bag.
4. Duplicate two *Candy Measurements* pages for each pair.

5. You may want to provide one set of candy that the children will be allowed to eat after completing the lesson. If you use unwrapped candy, discourage the children from eating the candy used in the lesson as it will be unsanitary from the handling.

Procedure

Part One: Sorting by Attributes

1. Divide the class into partners. Distribute the set of candy samples in the plastic bag to each group. Using the candy from the plastic bag, invite the students to sort the candy using their own rules.
2. Ask them to share the rules they used to sort the candy.
3. Direct the partners to now use your rules to sort their candy collection.
   • by firmness: hard, soft
   • by color
   • by shape
   • by length: long, short
   • by width: wide, narrow
4. Discuss which of their senses they used when they sorted the candy using the rules hard or soft. [touch] Record their responses on the chalkboard.
5. Continue the discussion for the different rules, asking the students to name the senses used each time. Add these responses to the chalkboard.
6. Direct each student to choose two different pieces of candy and to describe them by their similarities and differences.

Part Two: Matching by Touch

1. Tell the student pairs to place their candy samples in front of them.
2. Distribute the paper bags with the second set of candy samples.
3. Ask one of the partners to point to one sample of the candy in front of them. Direct the other partner to use only the sense of touch to find the matching candy inside the paper bag.
4. Before pulling the chosen sample out of the bag, ask him/her to describe how the candy feels.
5. After a description, tell him/her to pull out the candy to see if it is a direct match and then return the piece of candy to the bag.
6. Have the students take turns repeating procedures three through five with all four samples of candy.
7. As a class discussion, invite the students to describe their candy samples and to note anything they discovered using their sense of touch that they did not notice before.

Part Three: Comparing by Measuring

1. Using the set of candy in the plastic bag, direct each student to choose two different pieces of candy and to describe them by their similarities and differences.
2. Tell them to compare their candy samples, using only direct comparisons. (e.g., longer, shorter; round, long; etc.) Ask them to order their candy pieces from the shortest to the longest. Have the students write All/Some statements about the candy they have observed.
3. Suggest to the students that by using math/science tools, they will be able to learn more about their candy.
4. Give the students the *Sweet Sensations Measuring Tapes*, suggesting that this is a type of math tool. Ask them to measure the lengths of four pieces candy, not including the wrappers. (Discuss the proper method of measuring the length of the candy; where to place the candy on or next to the measuring tape, the position or direction of the candy, etc.)
5. Direct them to record the measurements by coloring in each measuring tape according to the measured length of each piece of candy. Tell the students to draw a picture of the candy on each tape to show which piece they are measuring. Have them cut the tapes apart.
6. Have the students order their *Sweet Sensations Measuring Tapes* from shortest to longest and glue them, in that order, onto the right column of the *Candy Measurements* page.
7. Direct the students to line up their actual samples in the same order as their measuring tapes and put them in the left column of the page. Invite them to compare the two columns. Discuss with the class how the measuring tapes are a representation of the same data as the actual candy pieces.
8. Repeat this procedure, directing the students to measure the width of each candy. Give them a second *Candy Measurements* page to record and compare the results.
9. Discuss what information they gathered about their candy that they didn't know before they used their measuring tool.

Part Four: Observing with aTtool

1. Using the same four pieces of candy, unwrap the candy and tell the students to use a hand lens to take a closer look.
2. Ask them to describe their candy and to note anything they can see using the hand lens. They should record their observations on a chart.
3. Tell the students to throw the unwrapped candy away since it has been handled.
4. Optional: Using a microscope, repeat procedures one through three.

Part Five: Enjoying the Candy

1. Direct the students to take the still wrapped candy out of the paper bag, unwrap it, and eat it.
2. Let the students take turns describing the flavor and the sweet, taste sensations.

Discussion

1. What information did you gather about your candy using your sense of sight? ...using your sense of touch? ...smell? ...hearing? ...taste?
2. What information did you gather about your candy by using the hand lens? ...the measuring tape?
3. How did the math/science tools help us learn about the candy?
4. How did our five senses help us learn about the candy?
5. Which pieces were the longest? Were there two pieces that were the same length?
6. How did you measure the pieces of candy? Explain.

Extensions

1. Bring in other thematic objects such as buttons, shells, rocks, etc. Tell the students to use their senses to observe and learn about the different samples. Be sure to use the hand lenses and microscopes with the objects as well.
2. Use the candy from the activity to decorate a gingerbread house or similar project.
3. Have the students use a balance to make direct comparisons of the masses of the candy pieces.
4. The measuring tools are divided in centimeter increments. You may want to number the units and ask the older students to record their measurements in centimeters.

*   Reprinted with permission from *Principles and Standards for School Mathematics,* 2000 by the National Council of Teachers of Mathematics. All rights reserved.

Dear Family,
   Our class would like to discover what we can learn from using our senses and math/science tools.
   We are gathering samples of a variety of wrapped candy which we will observe using our senses and tools such as measuring tapes and hand lenses. If possible, would you please help our class by donating a small bag of individually wrapped candy?

   Thank you for your help.

Please send the candy to school by

_____.

Dear Family,
   Our class would like to discover what we can learn from using our senses and math/science tools.
   We are gathering samples of a variety of wrapped candy which we will observe using our senses and tools such as measuring tapes and hand lenses. If possible, would you please help our class by donating a small bag of individually wrapped candy?

   Thank you for your help.

Please send the candy to school by

_____.

Sweet Sensations
Measuring Tapes

| 1 | 2 | 3 | 4 | 5 | 6 | 7 | 8 | 9 | 10 | 11 | |

| 1 | 2 | 3 | 4 | 5 | 6 | 7 | 8 | 9 | 10 | 11 | |

| 1 | 2 | 3 | 4 | 5 | 6 | 7 | 8 | 9 | 10 | 11 | |

| 1 | 2 | 3 | 4 | 5 | 6 | 7 | 8 | 9 | 10 | 11 | |

| 1 | 2 | 3 | 4 | 5 | 6 | 7 | 8 | 9 | 10 | 11 | |

| 1 | 2 | 3 | 4 | 5 | 6 | 7 | 8 | 9 | 10 | 11 | |

| 1 | 2 | 3 | 4 | 5 | 6 | 7 | 8 | 9 | 10 | 11 | |

| 1 | 2 | 3 | 4 | 5 | 6 | 7 | 8 | 9 | 10 | 11 | |

Draw the candy

Sweet Sensations Candy Measurements

Candy 1	🔔 glue measuring tape
Candy 2	🔔 glue measuring tape
Candy 3	🔔 glue measuring tape
Candy 4	🔔 glue measuring tape

EVERGREEN BRANCH

Topic
Observation

Key Question
How do different evergreen needles and branches compare?

Focus
Students will observe, compare, sort, classify, and graph evergreen branches and needles.

Guiding Documents
Project 2061 Benchmarks
- *Describing things as accurately as possible is important in science because it enables people to compare their observations with others.*
- *People can often learn about things around them by just observing those things carefully, but sometimes they can learn more by doing something to the things and noting what happens.*
- *Simple graphs can help to tell about observations.*

NRC Standard
- *Each plant or animal has different structures that serve different functions in growth, survival, and reproduction. For example humans have distinct body structures for walking, holding, seeing, and talking.*

NCTM Standard 2000*
- *Select an appropriate unit and tool for the attribute being measured*

Math
Graphing
Counting

Science
Life science
   plants
   diversity

Integrated Processes
Observing
Recording
Comparing and contrasting
Communicating
Classifying

Materials
For each student:
   evergreen branches with needles
   hand lens, optional
   name tag for branches

For the class:
   floor graph
   butcher paper for a wall graph
   package of 3 x 3 sticky notes
   yarn (for the name tags)

Background Information
An evergreen is a tree or a shrub that usually remains green all winter. Most evergreens are conifers. Conifers do not have true flowers; instead, they produce cones. Evergreens grow in areas where other trees cannot survive. Because of their special adaptations, they can grow in Arctic regions as well as desert regions.

Most evergreens have needle-like leaves rather than the broad leaves of the deciduous tree. The needles are tough, narrow-shaped, and have a waxy coat. The shape of the needles allows them to withstand wind and snow. Snow slides off the narrow needles and the waxy surface helps prevent freezing and drying out.

Each needle has only one or two veins which run the length of the needle. These veins transport the root sap and sugar sap that keep the tree alive. Evergreen needles make less food than broad leaves. However, evergreen needles do not fall all at once so they make food for a longer period.

Most evergreen needles can be grouped into three main categories: cluster needles (also known as bundled), single needles, and scaly leaves.
- Cluster needles are needles bundled by twos, threes, fives, tens, or more. The best known species of this group is the pine.
- Single needles are found on spruce and fir trees. Firs have single needles that grow opposite each other on the twig. Spruce needles are single needles that grow all around the twig.
- Scaly leaves resemble needles but are actually tiny, overlapping, scale-like petals, about one-eighth inch long. The twigs are hidden underneath the overlapping scales. The best known trees with scaly leaves are cedars, junipers, and cypress.

Management

1. This activity can be done shortly before or after the winter holidays, as students may have branches from Christmas trees that they can bring to school.

2. Send a letter to parents, explaining that you will be investigating evergreen branches. Ask parents to send a branch for their child to use in their study of evergreens. Evergreen branches stay fresh for quite a while so you can collect branches over a period of time. Make sure there is a variety as well as extras for students who may not be able to bring one.

3. Before you begin, if there is the variety of trees in the schoolyard, discuss the differences between evergreen and deciduous trees.

4. Bring in an evergreen branch to demonstrate to the students the appropriate method of obtaining a branch sample:
   - Because trees are living organisms, they should be handled with care. Never peel bark off a tree. The bark is the "skin" of the tree. Trees need their protective covering just as we do.
   - Carefully take the branch specimen from the tree using scissors or pruning shears. Encourage students to ask adults for assistance.
   - Students should be reminded to ask permission before gathering any branches.

5. Duplicate one *Name Tag* for each student to use to identify his/her branch.

Procedure

Part One

1. Ask the students to think about the evergreen trees they have seen around their homes, schools, and streets. Discuss the color, shape, and leaves of the evergreen. Compare the evergreen leaves with a leaf from a deciduous tree. Compare a branch from an evergreen tree with a branch from a deciduous tree.

2. Each child should have an evergreen branch. Help the students to observe their branches carefully. Hand lenses are helpful in this observation. Direct the discussion of the description of needles on the branch with such questions as the following:
   - How are the needles (leaves) attached to the branch?
   - How are the needles grouped on the branch?
   - Pull out a cluster and count the number of needles bundled together.

3. Tell the students to look closely at one needle from their branch, then ask them questions such as:
   - What color is it? Is it the same color on both sides? Is your needle the same color as your neighbors?
   - Feel the needle, is it smooth or prickly? Does it feel the same when it is rubbed both ways? Is it sharp on one end?
   - Smell the needle, does it have a scent? Crush the needle, does it now have a scent?
   - Find the vein in the needle. What do you observe about it?
   - How many sides does your needle have?

4. In a group, have students discuss their observations of their branches and compare their branches with others.

5. Then ask them to share their observations with the class. Record these observations on a large piece of paper or on the chalkboard.

6. Have each student draw a picture of his or her branch showing the physical details on the page entitled *Evergreen* or in their journals. Students will complete the page by describing how their branches feel.

7. Have each student write his or her name on a *Name Tag* and tie the name tag onto the branch. Do not try to classify the branch at this time.

Part Two

1. Invite the students to gather in a circle to play *In and Out of the Circle*. Select a student with a branch that has an obvious characteristic (e.g., smooth leaves or long skinny leaves). Have the child stand in the middle of the circle. Have all the students with similar branches stand together with the selected student. Invite the students to look at the branches within the circle, to determine whether the branches have the selected characteristic. Ask how many are in the circle. Have the students return to the outside of the circle.

2. Discuss other characteristics for other groupings.

3. Select another student whose branch has a different characteristic to stand in the circle and have students with similar branches group around that student. As students form a group holding their branches, encourage them to check to make sure the branches are like the selected one. Ask how many are in the circle.

4. Continue until each student has been in a group. Each time ask how many are in the circle.

5. Have each student return to the outside of the circle. Roll out a floor graph. Use the four labels, which are provided, on the graph.

6. After discussing each graph label, have students place their branches where they think they belong on the floor graph, making a real graph. Allow for discussion and analysis of the needles on the branches as cluster, single, and scaly to reinforce vocabulary.

7. After group discussion, have students remove their branches from the graph and write the classifications that correspond to those used on the floor graph on their name tags.

8. To extend the graph from the real to representational, give students 3 x 3 sticky notes and have them do crayon rubbings of a small portion of their branches and place the sticky notes on a wall graph. Use the same classification as used on the floor graph.

9. Have students display their branch specimens on a table for further observation during free time.

Discussion

1. Describe your evergreen branch.
2. Describe a needle from your branch.
3. How many in the class had a branch that graphed like yours?
4. Which group had the most?
5. Compare your branch with a branch from a deciduous tree. How is it different? How is it the same?
6. Name some things about your branch that you learned by observing carefully.

Extensions

1. Put the assorted evergreen branches on a table with a group of students and tell them to sort them according to type. Then have them write All/Some statements about the assortment.
2. Count the number of evergreens in your neighborhood, on your street or on your way to school.
3. Plant a sapling or small evergreen as a class project.
4. Find broadleaf evergreen samples in your neighborhood (holly, ivy, magnolia). Compare and contrast these to narrow evergreen needles.

Curriculum Correlation

Literature:
Read *The Little Fir Tree* by Hans Christian Andersen.

Art:
Use pine needles as brushes to paint pictures.

Social Studies:
Learn the history of how the evergreen became a Christmas symbol.

* Reprinted with permission from *Principles and Standards for School Mathematics,* 2000 by the National Council of Teachers of Mathematics. All rights reserved.

Dear Family,

Our class would like to do a scientific investigation of evergreen branches.

We need branches of different evergreen trees. We will be observing them using our senses, measuring tapes, and hand lenses.

If possible, could you send one evergreen branch with your child to use in our study?

Thank you for your help.

Please send the evergreen branch to school by

_____.

Dear Family,

Our class would like to do a scientific investigation of evergreen branches.

We need branches of different evergreen trees. We will be observing them using our senses, measuring tapes, and hand lenses.

If possible, could you send one evergreen branch with your child to use in our study?

Thank you for your help.

Please send the evergreen branch to school by

_____.

13

EVERGREEN BRANCH

My evergreen branch looks like this.

 My evergreen has these colors:

My evergreen smells like:

My evergreen feels like:

EVERGREEN BRANCH

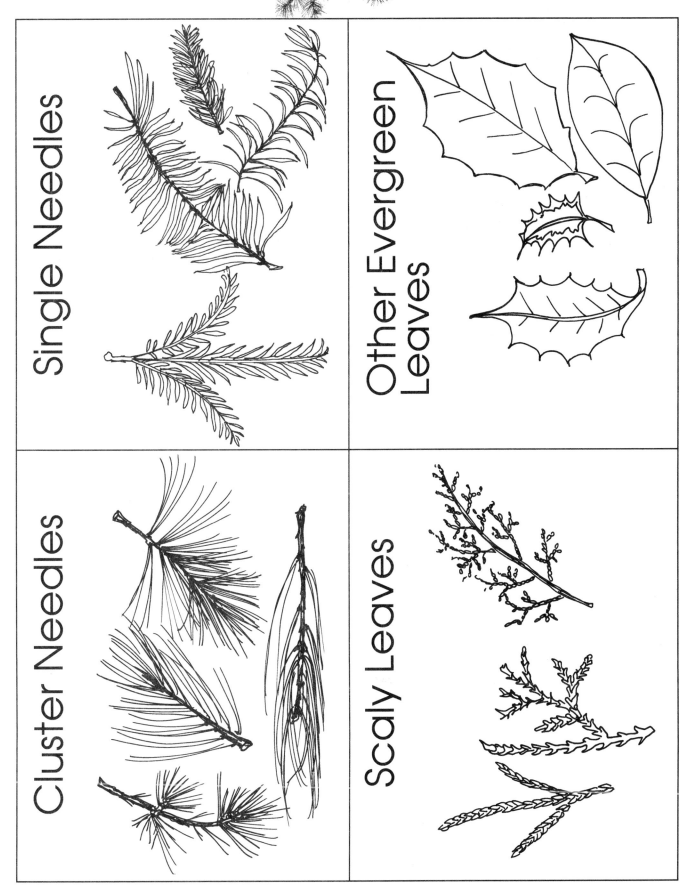

Single Needles

Other Evergreen Leaves

Cluster Needles

Scaly Leaves

Evergreen: _____

Owner's Name: _____

Name Tag

Evergreen: _____

Owner's Name: _____

Name Tag

Evergreen: _____

Owner's Name: _____

Name Tag

Evergreen: _____

Owner's Name: _____

Name Tag

Evergreen: _____

Owner's Name: _____

Name Tag

Evergreen: _____

Owner's Name: _____

Name Tag

A Close Look at Cones

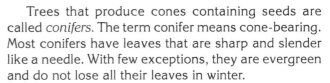

Topic
Observation

Key Questions
What can we discover about pine cones when we make careful observations? What makes a pine cone unique?

Focus
The students will make careful observations of pine cones to find details.

Guiding Documents
Project 2061 Benchmarks
• *Describing things as accurately as possible is important in science because it enables people to compare their observations with others.*
• *Draw pictures that correctly portray at least some features of the thing being described.*

NRC Standards
• *Scientists develop explanations using observations (evidence) and what they already know about the world (scientific knowledge).*
• *Communicate investigations and explanations.*

Integrated Processes
Observing
Comparing and contrasting
Collecting and recording data
Communicating

Materials
For each student:
1 pine cone (*see Management 1*)
journal

For the class:
a tray of common classroom objects (*see Management 2*)
a container to hold the pine cones

Background Information
This activity asks the students to use their observational skills to carefully observe a pine cone in order to distinguish it from a group of similar pine cones. The students discover how carefully they must attend to details and how accurately they must describe their pine cones if they are to distinguish theirs from others.

Trees that produce cones containing seeds are called *conifers*. The term conifer means cone-bearing. Most conifers have leaves that are sharp and slender like a needle. With few exceptions, they are evergreen and do not lose all their leaves in winter.

A cone, the seed bearing part of the conifer, is made up of wooden scales that overlap. Two seeds lie on top of one scale and are partly covered by the scale above. The scales are arranged spirally around the center of the cone. A tree that produces cones is called a gymnosperm, that means there is no ovary or fruit surrounding the seed. Instead, each seed develops between the scales of the female cone. A female immature cone is green and closed. As the cones mature, they dry and open allowing the seeds to fall out. Many of the seeds have thin, papery, wing-like structures that the wind can carry a long way. The male cones, located in clusters on the lower branches, produce pollen and then shrivel and fall off the tree within a few weeks.

Management
1. Collect at least one pine cone for each student in the class. Note: Pine cones are suggested here, but other objects such as leaves, rocks, apples, etc. could also be used.
2. Place five to ten common classroom objects (e.g., pencil, crayon, scissors, eraser, block, etc.) on a tray.
3. Prepare a journal for each student. Each journal will need a cover and two blank pages.

Procedure
Part One
1. Show the class a tray of objects. Hold up one object at a time and ask the class to describe the object using only the sense of sight to observe.
2. Invite a student to describe another object using several descriptive words without using the name of the object.
3. Ask another student to try to find the object described.
4. Discuss with the students how there is a difference between a *quick glance* at an object and a *careful observation* of an object. Discuss how they can learn many more things about an object through careful observation as compared to a quick glance. Define a quick glance by telling the students that it is when you look at something very quickly, not closely. A careful observation is a close observation of an object over an extended period of time.

Part Two

1. Show the class the container of pine cones. Hold up one pine cone and ask the students to describe all the things they observe about the pine cone. Tell them that you are giving them a quick glance at it.

2. Put it back in the container, mixing it with the others. Ask several of the students to try to find the one you were holding.

3. Ask why it was difficult to find the correct pine cone. Suggest that we do not always observe as carefully as we need to.

4. Give each student a pine cone. Ask the students to make very careful observations of their pine cones so that they will be able to identify their own. Give the class a few minutes to observe their cones. Direct the students to draw their pine cones and describe them in their journals.

5. Ask questions such as:
   - What shape is your pine cone?
   - Look at the edges. Are they straight or curved?
   - Is your pine cone more than one color? Does your picture show this?
   - Are there any broken parts to your pine cone? If so, describe them.

Part Three

1. Gather a group of five students. Collect the pine cones from these students. Place these cones on a tray in random order.

2. Invite each student to try to find his or her own pine cone from those on the tray. Ask the students to tell how they knew which one was their pine cone.

3. Repeat with five different students until all the students have had an opportunity to find their own pine cones.

Discussion

1. Why was it hard to find the first pine cone that was shown? [We didn't have time to look at it closely. It looked like all the others.]

2. Why was it easier to find your own pine cone? [We looked very closely and drew pictures of the pine cone. This helped us know more about pine cones.]

3. Did you observe more details about the pine cone when you just glanced at the cone or when you carefully observed the cone? Explain.

4. Describe your cone.

5. When you listen to your classmates describe their pine cones, do you begin to see them better? Explain.

6. Name some things about your pine cone that you discovered by observing it carefully that you did not see with a quick glance.

18

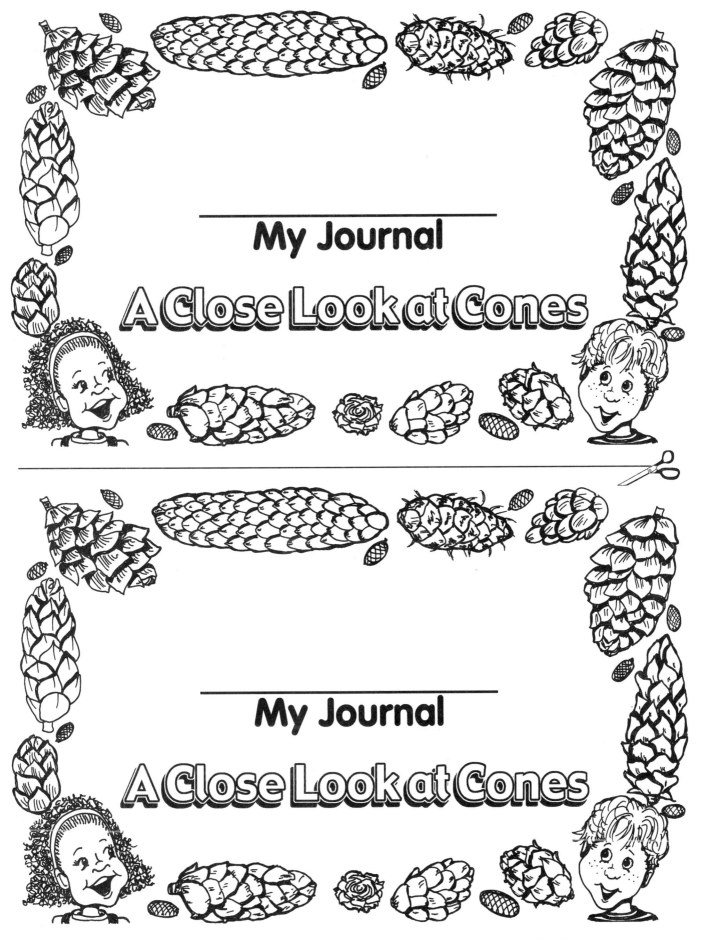

My Journal

A Close Look at Cones

My Journal

A Close Look at Cones

The Remarkable Peanut

Topic
Observing peanuts

Key Question
What can we learn about peanuts by using our senses and math and science tools?

Focus
The students will observe the physical properties of peanuts and group them according to certain attributes.

Guiding Documents
Project 2061 Benchmark
- *People can often learn about things around them by just observing those things carefully, but sometimes they can learn more by doing something to the things and noting what happens.*

NRC Standards
- *Describing things as accurately as possible is important in science because it enables people to compare their observations with those of others.*
- *Objects have many observable properties, including size, weight, shape, color, temperature, and the ability to react with other substances. Those properties can be measured using tools, such as rulers, balances, and thermometers.*

NCTM Standards 2000*
- *Understand how to measure using nonstandard and standard units*
- *Select an appropriate unit and tool for the attribute being measured*
- *Represent data using concrete objects, pictures, and graphs*

Math
Measurement
Number sense
Counting
Graphing
Estimating

Science
Life science
    human senses

Integrated Processes
Observing
Predicting
Collecting and recording data
Interpreting data
Comparing and contrasting

Materials
For Station 1: Observing Peanuts
    a bag of 10 peanuts per group
    hand lens or microscope
    balance
    mass units, customary or non-customary

For Station 2: Estimation and Counting
    a bag of 35 peanuts
    class graph

For Station 3: Balancing
    a bag of 20 peanuts
    balance
    Friendly Bears

For Station 4: Sink or Float
    3 peanuts per group
    bowl
    water
    paper towels

For Station 5: Measuring with peanuts
    a bag of 30 peanuts

For Station 6: Graphing
    a bag of 20 peanuts
    class graph

For Station 7: Handful of peanuts
    a bag of 20 peanuts

For Station 8: Making Peanut Butter
    a bag of peanuts
    blender
    spatula
    plastic spoon for each student
    soda crackers, optional

Background Information
    See *Peanut Fact* informational page.

Management

1. These activities are best done in small groups of four students.
2. Get a large bag of peanuts. (A one-pound (450 g) bag contains approximately 200 peanuts.) If possible, get peanuts that are different sizes and have several different numbers of peas in the shells. You will need approximately 400-500 peanuts.
3. Construct three class graphs, one for each of the Stations 2, 6, and 7.
4. Prepare a journal for each student.
5. The making of peanut butter at Station 8 should be a whole class activity. **Find out if there are any students that are allergic to peanuts. If there are, do NOT do this station activity.**
6. Read the story of *George Washington Carver* to the students and discuss his life and his discovery of the hundreds of uses of the peanut.

Procedure

1. Ask the students what they know about peanuts. Record their responses on a large sheet of butcher paper.
2. Hold up a bag of peanuts and ask, "What can we learn about peanuts?"
3. Ask the students what tools they will need to use in order to find out more about peanuts.
4. Tell the students that they will be go from station to station to do several activities that will allow them to observe and investigate peanuts.
5. Tell the students they are going to record their answers in their journals.

Station 1

What is a peanut?

1. For each group of students, have a small bag (ten) of unshelled peanuts. Tell the students that each one should pick one unshelled peanut out of the bag.
2. Invite students to "explore" an unshelled peanut with their fingers, nose, ears, and eyes. Ask them to not open the shell. Have a hand lens or microscope available for use.
3. Have the students discuss and describe their unshelled peanuts to each other.
4. After the students have been able to explore their peanuts, direct them to record in their journals their observations by drawing a picture of their peanut and describing it as to the size, shape, mass, texture, and color.

Station 2

How many peanuts are in the bag?

1. Place a bag of (35) peanuts in this station. Have students estimate how many peanuts are in the bag. Remind them to estimate the number of unshelled peanuts, not the number of peas in the shells.
2. Tell each group to record their estimate in their journal.
3. Have the students count the peanuts and record the amount as a whole number and as tens and ones.
4. Have two class graphs ready. Give each group a different color pen and have them graph their estimates on one graph and their actual results on the other. Discuss the results. Compare the actual results to the estimates.

Station 3

How many bears will balance?

1. Give each group of students a bag of 20 peanuts in the shells at this station. Have them count out 10 peanuts.
2. Ask the students to estimate and record in their journals how many Friendly Bears (or other non–customary unit) it will take to balance the 10 peanuts.
3. Have the students put ten peanuts in the shells in one pan of the balance. In the other pan, have them find how many Friendly Bears it takes to balance the peanuts. Ask them to record the actual results in their journals.
4. Now direct the students to estimate and record how many Friendly Bears will be needed to balance 20 peanuts in the shells. Have them find and record the actual results.
5. Tell the students to shell ten peanuts and estimate and record what they think the mass of the peanuts is now. Have them put the peas in the balance and determine the difference between their unshelled mass and the shelled mass.
6. Have the students compare the mass of the shelled peanuts with the mass of the shells only.
7. Direct the students to record their results in their journals.

Station 4

Will peanuts float or sink?

1. Give each group three peanuts.
2. Ask the students to predict what will happen when they put unshelled peanuts in a bowl of water.
3. Tell the students to pick three peanuts out of the bag and put them into a bowl of water. Discuss what happened to the peanuts.
4. Now tell the students to take the peanuts out of the water and shell them. Ask how many peas they have. Have them predict whether the peas will float. Allow time for the students to try floating the peanuts. Have them record their results.

Station 5
How long is a peanut?
1. Give each student a peanut.
2. Have each student compare the length of his or her peanut to the length of another student's peanut. Encourage the use of the terms *greater than, less than,* and *equal to.*
3. Invite the students to look around the room and find an object that is longer than their peanut.
4. Now direct them to find an object that is shorter than their peanut.
5. Challenge them to find something that is nearly the same size. Have them draw these objects and their peanuts in their journals.
6. Invite them to use their peanuts to determine the length of their desks in peanut units.
7. Ask the students to find out how many peanuts they will need to cover the page in their journal.

Station 6
How many peanuts in a shell?
1. Give the students a bag of 20 peanuts.
2. Ask them if they can figure out how many peas are in each shell.
3. Have them put the peanuts on the graph: those with one pea in the shell in the first column; those with two peas in the second column; and those with three peas in the third column; and if there are any with four peas, use the fourth column. Ask students which column has the most peas. ...the fewest peas.
4. As an extension, ask the students if they can find out what fractional part of the total has only one peanut, two peanuts, three peanuts, etc.

Station 7
How many peanuts are in a handful?
1. Give the students a bag of 20 peanuts.
2. Tell the students to dump the peanuts out on the table and look at them. Invite the students to estimate how many they can pick up in one hand. Have them record their estimate on the class graph.
3. Direct the students to pick up as many peanuts as they can, count them, and record their results on the class graph in a different color next to their estimates.
4. Tell the students to record their results in their journal.

Station 8
How do you make peanut butter?
1. Shell enough peanuts to have $1\frac{1}{2}$ cups of shelled peas. (This will yield $\frac{3}{4}$ of a cup of peanut butter).
2. Put the shelled peas in the blender or food processor.
3. Turn the blender on and let it run for several minutes. Stop the blender occasionally to scrape the sides and around the blades with a spatula.
4. It will take about five minutes to start creaming. Continue to blend until the peanut butter is the consistency you prefer.
5. Repeat the procedure if you want more peanut butter or if you have more than 25 students in your class.
6. Serve it to the students. If you prefer, give the students crackers on which to spread the peanut butter.
7. Ask the students to record in their journals what they think the peanut butter tastes like.

Discussion
1. Describe how your peanut looks, its color and size.
2. Describe how your peanut feels. Is it rough? ...smooth? ...bumpy? Does it have ridges?
3. Is there something in the shell? How do you know?
4. What does the peanut smell like?
5. What was the most common number of peas in one shell?
6. What do you feel makes the peanut float?

Extension
1. Make up a bag of peanuts of mixed sizes. Have students reach into the bag and without looking predict how many nuts are in the shell of the peanut they have in their hand.
2. If appropriate, discuss the parts of the peanut plant.

Curriculum Correlation
Art:
    Dye the peanuts in the shells with food coloring and alcohol. Use the resulting colored peanuts in an art project such as a mosaic.

Music:
    Sing some songs that have to do with peanuts: "Goober Peas," " I Found a Peanut," "Peanut, Peanut Butter."

* Reprinted with permission from *Principles and Standards for School Mathematics,* 2000 by the National Council of Teachers of Mathematics. All rights reserved.

Peanut Facts

Scientific name:
	Family:	Leguminosae
	Genus:	Arachis
	Species:	Hypogaea

Food Value:
Fat	47.5%
Protein	26.0%
Carbohydrates	18.6%
Water	5.6%
Other	2.3%

Peanuts are the fruit of the peanut plant. Although they look and taste like nuts, they are really a kind of pea—a pea that grows underground. The spongy, dimpled peanut shells are actually pods that usually contain two peas, but can contain from one to five. Peanuts are often called ground nuts, but are also called goobers, goober peas, ground peas, and pindas.

Peanut plants are annuals that grow in warm sandy places. The vines grow to about 2 feet tall and 3-4 feet wide. Peanuts are usually planted in May and harvested in October. The plants have yellow flowers that blossom for 2 to 3 months. The flowers open at sunrise, are pollinated by noon, soon wither, and fall off. A green peg will emerge from the withered flower and it will grow downward into the soil to a depth of 1 to 3 inches. The tips of the pegs swell and mature into pods. When the plant begins to turn brown, it is time to harvest the peanuts. The entire plant is pulled out of the grounds. The p ods are allowed to dry and are then pulled off. Some pods are saved for planting next year's crop.

None of the peanut plant is wasted. The plant itself is used for livestock feed. One-half of all peanuts is turned into peanut butter. One-fourth of all peanuts is roasted and salted for human consumption. Peanut oil is used in salad dressings, soaps, face powders, shaving creams, and shampoos. Even the shells are ground into powder and used in wallboards, plastics, and abrasives.

The next time that you eat a peanut, open up one of the small peas. It will usually split in half easily. On one side there will be a tiny peanut plant, an embryo just waiting for the right conditions to grow.

Peanut Plant

leaf

peanut pods

roots

peg

flower

Peanuts
Discovery Journal

by: _____

I think peanuts are:

1. What is a peanut?

Describe your 🥜

Size _____   Color _____

Shape _____   Feel _____

Observation
_____

2. How many 🥜 are in the bag?

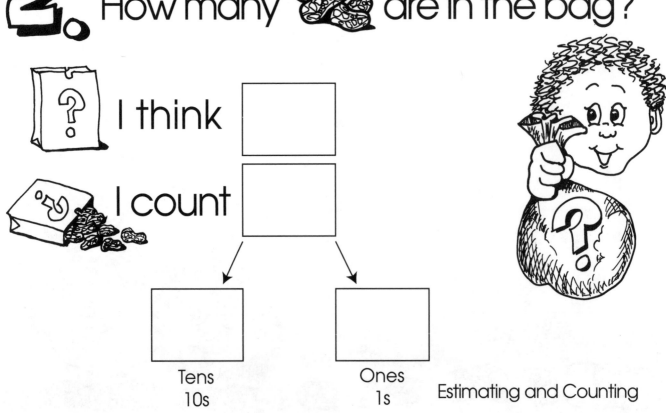

I think [ ]

I count [ ]

Tens
10s

Ones
1s

Estimating and Counting

3. How many bears will balance?

	I think:	I count:
10 peanuts in shells		
20 peanuts in shells		
10 peanuts without shells		

Finding the Mass

4. Will peanuts float or sink?

I think

 _____ will float or sink.

_____ does float or sink.

I think

 _____ will float or sink.

 _____ do float or sink.

Density

5. How long is a peanut?

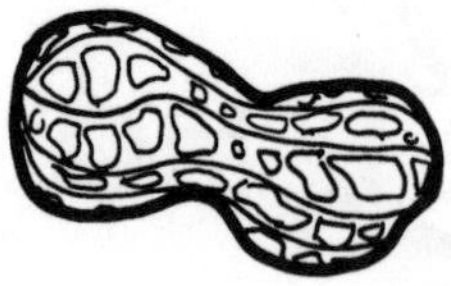

Compare		
longer than		
shorter than		
same as		

Measure

How many 🥜 long is your desk? ☐

How many 🥜 will cover this page? ☐

Measurement

6. How many peanuts in a shell?

6				
5				
4				
3				
2				
1				
	one	two	three	four

Graphing

7. How many peanuts are in a handful?

I think I can pick up [ ]

1	2	3	4	5	6	7	8	9	10	11	12	13	14	15	16	17	18

I can pick up [ ]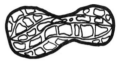

1	2	3	4	5	6	7	8	9	10	11	12	13	14	15	16	17	18

Mark the class graph.

Volume

---

8. What is peanut butter?

 + 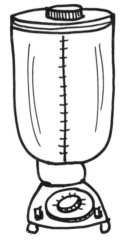  =

Measure 1½ cups of shelled peanuts.

I think peanut butter tastes

yum!   ok   yuk!

George Washington Carver

George Washington Carver was a man who was interested in the world around him. Carver spent a lot of time finding products that could be produced from peanuts. During his career, he made approximately 300 products from the peanut. They ranged from food products of beverages, dyes, chili sauce, mayonnaise, and vinegar to medicine such as iron tonic, laxatives, and tannic acid. Carver used every part of the peanut. Wall boards, paper, animal feeds, axle grease, and plastics were some of the things produced from the hulls, skins, and vines of the peanut.

George Washington Carver was a sickly child. He lost his mother to kidnappers at an early age. A German immigrant couple by the name of Carver raised him and his brother Jim.

During his early years with the Carvers, George began his lifelong love affair with plants. He wanted to know about every strange stone, flower, insect, bird, or animal. He did not have access to any book that could give him answers to all the questions he had, so he had to find the answers by studying the plants and animals themselves.

He had a desperate hunger for education. He went from school to school learning all he could before moving on to another place. He graduated from Iowa State University and was offered a job there as a professor. However, a letter came from Tuskeegee Institute in Alabama asking Carver to come and train students to be teachers, farmers, and technicians. Carver, remembering his childhood and his quest for education, accepted this offer and returned to the South to help his people.

On his way to his new job, he looked out the window of the train and all he could see was cotton, cotton, and more cotton. Cotton grew everywhere, but it was very poor cotton, not even worth picking. The land looked sick and tired. The people looked tired and sick.

George was determined that he would teach his students how to improve the land and show them how to grow nutritious crops. He started by taking the students around the neighborhood collecting old bottles, jars, chipped cups, any throw aways; these became the equipment for his lab. Next he led the class to the school dump where a gigantic pumpkin vine was growing. Here he explained that there was no finer fertilizer than the food scraps we throw away. He showed the class how to make a compost pile. They grew cowpeas which put minerals back into the soil that cotton had taken out of it. George knew how to cook the cowpeas into nutritious food that the class enjoyed. Next they planted sweet potatoes. When the potatoes were harvested, he and his students worked out a hundred new ways in the lab to use the crop. Some of the things they discovered that could be made from the sweet potatoes were fine laundry starch, good quality flour, and syrup.

Perhaps some of George's most important investigations were in the uses of peanuts. His discoveries turned a crop that was used only for food into an economically important agricultural product.

George Washington Carver

THE GINGERBREAD MAN

Topic
Looking at attributes, making sense of data, exploring money values, problem solving

Key Questions
How can we sort the gingerbread men after looking carefully at them? How will you decide what to purchase to decorate your gingerbread man?

Focus
Primary students will use observational skills to sort gingerbread men, graph them, and measure them. They will use problem-solving skills in purchasing objects to use to decorate the gingerbread men.

Guiding Documents
Project 2061 Benchmarks
• *Describing things as accurately as possible is important in science because it enables people to compare their observations with others.*
• *People can often learn about things around them by just observing those things carefully, but sometimes they can learn more by doing something to the things and noting what happens.*

NCTM Standards 2000*
• *Sort, classify, and order objects by size, number, and other properties*
• *Recognize, describe, and extend patterns such as sequences of sounds and shapes or simple numeric patterns and translate from one representation to another*
• *Understand how to measure using nonstandard and standard units*
• *Measure with multiple copies of units of the same size, such as paper clips laid end to end*
• *Use tools to measure*

Math
Measuring
Graphing
Patterning
Sorting
Problem solving
Using money
Estimating

Integrated Processes
Observing
Comparing and contrasting
Communicating
Collecting and recording data
Organizing data

Materials
For the class:
the book *The Gingerbread Man* (see *Bibliography*)
Unifix cubes or meter tape
ingredients for gingerbread cookies (recipe provided)
cooking equipment (bowls, spoons)
floor graph (see *Management 9*)

For the store:
7 containers, one for each of the following items:
rickrack
buttons
sequins
beads
raisins
pipe cleaners
red hot candies
money cards (*see Management*)
80 pennies, play or actual (see *Management 8*)
8 plastic cups

For each student:
small paper bag for shopping
envelope for money
coins
Gingerbread People Patterns
brown construction paper
gingerbread man stencil (*see Management 12*)
scissors
glue
crayons

Background Information
Students will carefully observe each gingerbread man, looking for similarities and differences. After brainstorming attributes, primary students will explore ways to sort and organize this observed information. This sorting and organizing helps them develop useful skills they will rely on when dealing with similarities and diversities in their world. Frequently primary students sort a collection of items once and feel they have explored all possible ways in which to organize the items. In this activity students are asked to sort the collection of gingerbread men at least three ways.

This activity gives the students an opportunity to spend a designated amount of money for a variety of objects, thereby challenging the students in problem solving, estimation, and mental math skills. They will find they need to use problem-solving skills to get the best buys for their personal designs for their gingerbread men.

The baking experience allows the children to observe change. They will begin to recognize what happens to matter when it interacts with heat energy. They will also apply the use of measurement in cooking.

This activity integrates many different curriculum areas. The making of gingerbread cookies is an appropriate activity any time of the year. It can provide a festive holiday unit in place of the traditional activities and parties.

Management

1. Get a copy of the story *The Gingerbread Man*.
2. This activity is divided into four sections that can be done on four different days.
3. Make a large *Gingerbread People* chart with three columns so the students can compare their attributes. Label the columns: *Patterns, Student Decorated,* and *Baked.*

Gingerbread People		
Patterns	Student Decorated	Baked
big smiles little smiles bows buttons arms — up/out/down standing running hair/no hair boys girls	eyes - beads dots yarn hair cloth rickrack glitter	icing hair brittle hard spicy raisin eyes big smiles

4. If desired, copy the *Gingerbread People Patterns* on brown card stock and laminate so they can be used each year. The patterns can be reduced to provide opportunities for the students to make their own pattern strips.
5. During the pattern sorting, students should work in pairs. The pattern strip experience is best done individually.
6. Collect the items you will be using to decorate the paper gingerbread men and place them into separate containers. Self-closing bags, plastic containers, or small boxes work well. A list of suggested items appears in the *Materials* section.

7. Prepare money cards to represent the assigned cost of each item. Next to each container of decorative items, place the appropriate money card and an empty cup. Price the items for the store so the students can't buy one of each, but must use problem-solving skills to afford what they want for their gingerbread man.
8. Give each kindergarten child 10 cents to buy items and each first-grade student 25 cents. The money will be used at the store by small groups of children.
9. Make a floor graph of 5 x 10 grids and tape it to the floor. The blocks of the grid should be slightly larger than the gingerbread man stencil.
10. The making of the real cookies can be an option for the winter holiday party. Parents who would normally donate goodies can be asked to send in the ingredients, cookie sheets, etc. On the day of the party, the children's treats would be their personally-made gingerbread men.
11. In the measurement section of this activity, it is desirable for each child to make a "life-sized" gingerbread man to experience larger size measurement. The teacher could also make one "life-sized" gingerbread figure and let students do the measurement at a learning center. Use an overhead projector to enlarge the gingerbread man stencil to 90 cm x 70 cm.
12. Copy the *Gingerbread Man Stencil* on card stock and cut it out. The heavier paper makes it easier for students to trace around it.

Procedure

Part One: Gingerbread People to Sort and Pattern
1. Read several versions of the book *The Gingerbread Man* so students can discuss the similarities and differences in the plots, characters, and illustrations of the versions.
2. Give each pair of students a set of the *Gingerbread People Patterns*. The students can color the gingerbread people if they wish. Have the class brainstorm the observed characteristics. They will observe attributes such as those with eyeglasses, ears, big noses, small smiles, etc. You may wish to use a large silhouette of a gingerbread man for this brainstorming list. Record the students' answers on the *Gingerbread People* chart in the column labeled *Patterns*. Then have the students write All/Some statements about the gingerbread men (e.g., *All* the gingerbread people are brown and have eyes. *Some* of the gingerbread people have smiles and have hair.)

3. Ask students to sort their gingerbread characters by attributes in one way. Tell them to share the ways they sorted and organized. Ask the students to put them back into one set and sort again by a new attribute. Invite them to again share the ways they sorted. Brainstorm new ways to sort, then have them sort and do it one more time.

4. Suggest that the students play the game *What's My Rule?* by sorting the gingerbread people and having their partners guess the rule (attributes) by which they sorted the gingerbread people. For example, those with big smiles/those with little smiles; those with ears/those with no ears; those with a big nose/those with a small nose.

5. Have the students explore ways to create patterns using the gingerbread people. Suggest that they share their patterns with the class. Primary students enjoy chanting the patterns, (up, up, down; big nose, big nose, big nose, tiny nose, tiny nose; etc.) Tell them to decide on one pattern and glue it on a pattern strip. Suggest the students can wear their pattern strip as a headband.

Part Two: Gingerbread Men to Decorate

1. Give a 9 x 12 inch piece of brown construction paper and the gingerbread stencil to each student. Instruct the students to trace the stencil onto the brown paper and cut the gingerbread person out. Tell them they will decorate their gingerbread person with trimmings from "the store."

2. Discuss with them about using money to purchase trimmings at the store to decorate their gingerbread people. Tell the students that they will each have a certain amount of money—10 cents for Kindergarten students and 25 cents for first-grade students—to go shopping at the classroom store for items to decorate their gingerbread people. Point out that some of the items will cost more than one penny. Explain that they need to think about what they want on their gingerbread person and what they can afford before they come to the store. Have them bring their gingerbread person to the station.

3. Give each student the appropriate money in an envelope and a shopping bag.

4. Ask the students if they will be able to buy one of all the items for sale with their money. Have them explain their answers.

5. Use this opportunity to ask the prices of certain items: How much for two raisins? How much for rickrack? How much money would be needed to buy one of every item that is for sale?

6. Allow students to shop in small groups. Tell them to follow this procedure: place their money on the money cards, pick out the items they are purchasing. Place the items into their shopping bags, and deposit the money from the money card into the cup representing the "cash register" next to each item.

7. Once the students have used all their money, instruct them to go to another table and begin to use their purchases to decorate their gingerbread persons.

8. After the gingerbread persons have dried, have students bring them to the floor graph. They will compare their previously brainstormed list of characteristics with their new gingerbread creations. Add any new attributes to the *Gingerbread People* chart in the column *Student Decorated*.

9. Use these gingerbread creations to decorate the room or a class tree by punching a hole and attaching a piece of yarn for a hanger.

Part Three: Cooking and Science of Gingerbread Men

1. Using the *Gingerbread Recipe*, have the students make their own gingerbread cookies. Let students be a part of the measuring and mixing of the gingerbread cookie recipe. It is recommended that this be done in a circle on the rug, if possible, so all the students can actually observe the measurement and mixing processes.

2. Get the students to think about what is going to happen to the dough in the cookies when they are placed in the oven. Will the dough stay the same? How will it change?

3. Ask the students to discuss attributes while they are trimming their own unbaked cookies with red hots, raisins, and other decorative candies. Ask them to predict what will happen to the decorations when placed in the oven.

4. When the cookies come out of the oven, discuss the changes the students observe.

5. After the cookies are made, students may enjoy exploring the similarities and differences in attributes of the baked cookies before eating them. Add any new attributes to the *Gingerbread People* chart under the column *Baked*. Discuss what the cookies looked like before and after baking. Ask the students what they think heat does to the unbaked cookies.

Part Four: Child-Sized Gingerbread People to Measure

1. This part has two options. One: if using only one gingerbread child, place it in a learning startion so that students can determine its measurements. Tell the students not to share the information until the entire class has visited the learning center. Option Two: Let each student make a life-size gingerbread child.

34

2. Make a gingerbread child by using a transparency of the gingerbread man stencil on the overhead projector. Move the projector until you obtain the appropriate child–like size—approximately 90 cm in height with an arm span of 70 cm. (Option Two: Have the students make their own gingerbread children by tracing around this enlarged pattern.)

3. Use the one giant stencil to cut double copies out of butcher paper. Staple both copies together around the perimeter of the gingerbread person leaving enough space to stuff with shredded newspaper and then finish stapling the remainder.

4. (Option Two: Have the students use trim and decorations, or they can decorate the gingerbread children with crayons and colored markers.)

5. Using this life-sized gingerbread child, suggest that the students make estimates of its height and arm span in Unifix cubes. Have them measure the gingerbread child and record the actual height and arm span measurement. Use a variety of manipulatives to measure the gingerbread child over and over. Let students measure how long the row of buttons is and how wide a smile the gingerbread child has. Tell the students to record their results on the sheet *Gingerbread Child Measure*.

Discussion

1. What were some ways you sorted your gingerbread patterns?

2. How did your sorting differ from the other groups in the class?

3. How did the observed attributes differ in the gingerbread people made of paper from those made of actual cookie dough?

4. If we were able to graph our actual cookies, how might the graph look?

5. When baked, what made the cookies change? [heat]

6. Which decoration on the gingerbread cookies changed the most? Why?

7. Describe the changes made in your gingerbread cookie when it was baked.

8. In the story, the Gingerbread Man jumps on the fox to get across the river and is eaten. What would you have done if you were a Gingerbread Man?

Extension

An important step for young students is to give them a pattern such as A, A, B in letters and have the class explore all the ways they can create that pattern using the gingerbread men. Let the students discuss the many ways they created a pattern.

Curriculum Correlation

Math
Make gingerbread houses out of graham crackers, piped with thick frosting and decorated with candies. (The directions for the construction and recipes for the frosting of a graham cracker gingerbread house can be found in many holiday cookbooks.) Ask the students to think about shapes and parts of shapes. A square graham cracker when broken in half is two rectangles, two squares put together to make a pointed roof forms a triangle, small silver balls are spheres. The gingerbread houses and gingerbread men can be used as holiday decorations on a shelf with a base created from cotton snow. A school lunch milk carton can be used as the framework of the house with frosting used to glue the graham crackers to the carton to form the house. Candy from *Sweet Sensations* can be used to decorate the gingerbread houses.

Language Arts
Have the students write their own gingerbread stories, explaining who would chase them and how they would escape. Make the writing paper by making writing lines on the gingerbread man stencil.

Assessment

Have students explain orally (teacher can record) or describe in writing, how they would construct a graph using their baked gingerbread cookies. Have them actually design a graph on grid paper.

Bibliography

Amoss, Berthe. *The Cajun Gingerbread Boy.* Hyperion Books for Children. New York. 1994.

Aylesworth, Jim. *The Gingerbread Man.* Scholastic, Inc. New York. 1998.

Galdone, Paul. *The Gingerbread Man.* Houghton Mifflin. Boston. 1975.

Kassirer, Sue. *The Gingerbread Boy.* Random House. New York. 1993.

Kimmel, Eric A. *The Gingerbread Man.* Holiday House. New York. 1994.

36

THE GINGERBREAD MAN

People Patterns

THE GINGERBREAD MAN

We caught a big Gingerbread Child.

Now I plan to measure it.

This is the unit I used: _____

	My estimate	My measure
Height		
Head		
Leg		
Arm		
Arm Span		

Run! Run! Fast as you can!

You can't catch me!

I'm the Gingerbread Man!

Gingerbread Recipe

Mix: $\frac{1}{2}$ cup soft margarine

$1\frac{1}{2}$ cups brown sugar
(packed)

$2\frac{1}{4}$ cups molasses

Stir in: 1 cup cold water

Sift together and add to mixture:

$10\frac{1}{2}$ cups of flour

3 teaspoons baking powder

$1\frac{1}{2}$ teaspoons salt

$1\frac{1}{2}$ teaspoons allspice

$1\frac{1}{2}$ teaspoons ginger

$1\frac{1}{2}$ teaspoons cloves

$1\frac{1}{2}$ teaspoons cinnamon

Bake in a 350° oven for 12-15 minutes.

Decorate.

I made a Gingerbread Child
With chubby red hot cheeks;
The eyes were silver bobbles,
The nose a raisin piece.
I piped my child with frosting
As white as winter snow.
Mom baked him in the oven;
The baking time passed slow.
When we took him out of the oven,
He was dark brown from the heat.
His body puffed and glossy;
He looked too good to eat!

--Barbara Novelli

What is My Rule?

I put my gingerbread people in two groups.

Topic
Place Value

Key Question
How much does your mitten hold?

Focus
Students will explore the concept of place value and volume.

Guiding Documents
Project 2061 Benchmark
* *Numbers can be used to count things, place them in order, or name them.. Those properties can be measured using tools, such as rulers, balances, and thermometers.*

NCTM Standards 2000*
* *Recognize the attributes of length, volume, weight, mass, area, and time,*
* *Represent data using concrete objects, pictures, and graphs*

Math
Estimation
Volume
Place value
Symmetry

Integrated Processes
Observing
Comparing and contrasting
Collecting and recording data
Interpreting data

Materials
For each student:
   mittens (either real or ones made of paper)

For the class:
   the book *The Mitten* by Jan Brett or *The Mitten*
     by Alvin Tresselt
   assorted items such as:
     Unifix cubes
     Teddy Bear Counters
     milk caps
     bottle caps
     tiles
     crayons or felt tip markers

Background Information
As weather turns cold, children often come to school wearing mittens. Two versions of an Ukranian folktale, *The Mitten*, provide a basis for an integrated primary classroom unit. The rich language and beautiful illustrations in each of these books help to develop a powerful vocabulary base and vivid mental images. The science concepts developed may include: adaptations to winter weather, insulating effects, and changes in states of matter. In mathematics, this activity addresses six strands: logic, statistics, number, pattern, geometry, and measurement.

The capacity of a mitten is explored through fitting items of the same size into it. Mittens made of materials that will expand have greater capacities. Students will also compare the sizes of the items that are being put into the mitten and the number that will fit.

In *Part Two* of this activity, the idea of line symmetry is introduced with the reproduction of mitten patterns. The students will sort the mittens into sets using a Venn diagram.

Management
1. Send a letter home to the parents asking them to send a pair of mittens to school with their children. Make sure you have extra mittens for the children who cannot bring a pair. Garage sales or thrift shops are sources of inexpensive mittens.
2. An alternative to real mittens would be paper mittens made by making two from a stencil and stapling or stitching the two pieces together.
3. Use a collection of manipulatives to fit into the mittens, such as: Teddy Bear Counters, Unifix cubes, tiles, and bottle caps that have a consistent size.
4. For *Part Three* check the students' mittens, if they do not have enough different patterns, give each child a mitten pattern to cut out and design paper mittens.
5. When students are designing their mittens for the symmetry experience, all must have the same resources to use (e.g., crayons or felt tip markers). Encourage the students to make a simple pattern rather than a detailed project.

Procedure

Part One

1. Begin this activity by reading the Ukrainian folktale *The Mitten.* Both Alvin Tresselt's and Jan Brett's versions provide a delightful base for this activity. If possible, read the two versions of this folktale and let the students discuss the similarities and differences between the two.

2. Prepare sentence strips with sentences from the mitten story. Read both stories a second time, then give the students time to sequence the sentences in a pocket chart and dramatize the story. Let certain members of the class hold a sentence and put it in the pocket chart as others act out that part of the story. Using a blanket as a mitten, repeat again and again!

3. As the students sequence and review the story, let them add their own language and art work. Make paper mittens using the pattern in the lesson and have the students add pictures of the animals as they retell the story.

Part Two

1. Introduce the concept of capacity as *the amount of space that can be filled.*

2. Have the students look at and describe the items they will use for filling their mittens.

3. Record the attributes of the items as the students describe their observations. The students should include the relative size of each item and make an estimation as to the number of items of each type they can fit into the mitten.

4. Have the students work in pairs to first estimate how many of a specific unit (Unifix cube, bottle cap) they will be able to fit into their mitten and record on the activity page. Remind them to write the name of the unit of measure for the first set. Younger students can sketch the unit.

5. Invite them to fill the mitten to capacity. After filling it, tell the students to empty and sort the contents into tens and ones and record their count on the recording sheet. They can proceed to doing another mitten or unit of measure.

6. Ask the students to come to the group gathering to share their results.

7. After listening to the class reports, have the students record their own conclusions about units of measure and the capacities of different mittens.

Part Three

1. Invite the students to look carefully at their mittens and those of their classmates. Encourage them to notice the color, design, material, and patterns of the mittens.

2. Tell the students they are going to sort the mittens in whichever way they wish, but they must explain and justify their method of sorting.

3. Set up circles for Venn diagrams and sort the mittens into sets according to similar attributes. Have the students count the number of mittens in each circle and in the intersection. Ask them if it is necessary to have an intersection.

Part Four

1. Copy one mitten pattern for each student. Let the students create their own designs on one of the paper mittens.

2. Have them trade mittens with a partner and then try to copy the design of the partner's mitten to create a symmetric match, making one mitten the mirror image of the other. This introduces the idea of line symmetry in which the first mitten is on one side of the line and the second is a reflection on the other side.

Discussion

1. If you were to rewrite this story using other animals, what ones would you choose? Would they fit in your mitten better? Explain.

2. What unit of measure (item) did you use? Describe it.

3. How did you sort and count units?

4. Does how a mitten is constructed or what it is made of have anything to do with how many items will fit into the mitten? Explain.

5. Does how you fit units into the mitten have anything to do with the actual numbers of items that fit? Explain.

6. What difficulties did you have in making a symmetric match with your partner's mitten?

Curriculum Coorelation

Literature:

Brett, Jan. *The Mitten.* G. P. Putnam's Sons. New York. 1989.

Tresselt, Alvin. *Mitten: An Old Ukranian Folktale.* Mulberry Books. New York. 1989.

Extensions

1. Have the students relate their experiences with bottle caps, Unifix cubes, etc. to the animals in the story. What would happen if only mice wanted in the mitten? ...bears?

2. Have the students find the mitten that held the greatest number of items in the class. ...the least.

Home Link

Encourage the students to tell the story of the mittens and the animals at home to their parents.

What fits in a Mitten?

1. Choose a unit to put inside a mitten.

2. How many units will a mitten hold?

I predict:

What I put in the mitten:

I count:

tens   ones

I predict:

What I put in the mitten:

I count:

tens   ones

3. Tell about what you discovered.

A Fit Mitten

Molly, Alli, and Tommy Kitten all wear different colored mittens.

1. Tommy does not wear a mitten the color of a stop sign.

2. Molly likes to wear stripes.

	blue	red	striped
Molly			
Tommy			
Alli			

Which mitten belongs to which Kitten?

blue: _____   red: _____   striped: _____

A Fit Mitten

Who's in the Mitten?

All these animals are hiding in the mitten. What is their order?

Clues

1. The first one inside the mitten is the smallest animal.
2. The last one in is the largest animal.
3. Owl is between Rabbit and Mole.
4. The carrot eater is next to Mouse.

1. First	2. Second	3. Third	4. Fourth	5. Fifth	6. Sixth

cut

Rabbit	Mole	Mouse	Bear	Owl	Wolf

cut

Mitten Patterns

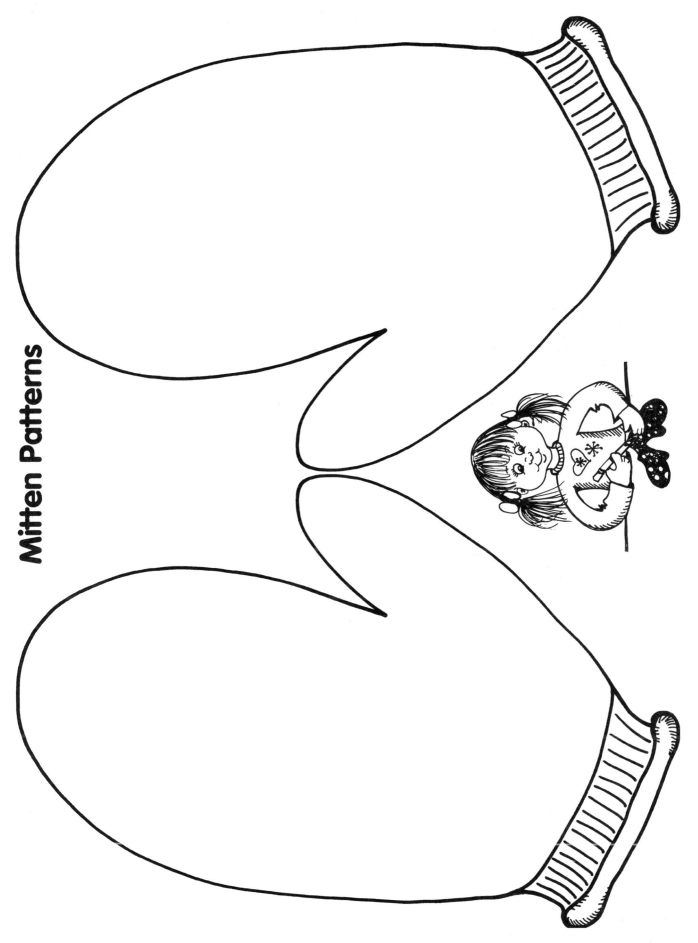

FROSTY FORMS

Topic
Physical change in matter

Key Question
How does the shape of ice affect how fast or slow it melts?

Focus
The students will observe ice as it melts and note the differences in melting rates of various shaped ice formations.

Guiding Documents
Project 2061 Benchmarks
- *Shapes such as circles, squares, and triangles can be used to describe many things that can be seen.*
- *Things change in some ways and stay the same in some ways.*
- *Heating and cooling cause changes in the properties of materials.*

NRC Standards
- *Scientists develop explanations using observations (evidence) and what they already know about the world (scientific knowledge).*
- *Communicate investigations and explanations.*

NCTM Standards 2000*
- *Recognize the attributes of length, volume, weight, area, and time*
- *Compare and order objects according to these attributes*

Math
Geometry
    shape
Measurement
    time
    capacity

Science
Physical science
    matter
      physical change

Integrated Processes
Observing
Collecting and recording data
Comparing and contrasting
Communicating
Generalizing

Materials
For each group of students:
    a variety of containers (see *Management 1*)
    an ice cube
    pie tin (see *Management 3*)
    2 empty film canisters (see *Management 4*)

For the class:
    access to a freezer
    masking tape
    salt
    Which one will melt first? graph (see *Management 5*)
    2 ribbon markers
    graphing markers (see *Management 5*)
    camera, optional

Background Information
Students will observe the physical change that takes place as ice melts into liquid water. The addition of heat causes this change to take place. Heat is added to the ice when it is taken out of the freezer and allowed to come to room temperature. When heat is taken away from the water, such as by placing it in a freezer, the water will turn to ice.

Liquid water takes on the shape of the container and can be poured. Solid water—ice—will keep its shape as long as it remains a solid. It cannot be poured.

The melting rate of ice is dependent upon its surrounding temperature and the amount of exposed surface area. Keeping all other variables the same, it can be generalized that the greater the exposed surface area, the faster the rate of melting.

This investigation develops conceptually as it progresses. *Part One* has students timing the melting rate of same size, same shape ice cubes. *Part Two* invites them to use the same volume of water in different-shaped containers to make ice. They then determine the melting rates to conclude that there are differences. *Part Three* allows students to combine different shapes (different surface areas) of ice to make ice castles and to predict the time required for them to melt.

Management
1. Prior to the lesson, collect a variety of containers suitable to put in the freezer. For example, jar lids, margarine containers, paper cups, etc. Be sure to have many different sizes. When making the ice castles, each group will need at least three containers.
2. For *Part One*, bring in an ice cube for each group of four students.
3. Gather one pie tin large enough to hold the ice castle made by each group. The pie tins will be used in *Parts One* and *Three* of the investigation. To simplify the identification of the pie tins, label the bottom of each with letters of the alphabet: A, B, C, etc.

4. For *Part Two,* each group will need a different-sized container to which they will add the same amount of water (one filled film canister) that will need to be frozen. For *Part Three,* partially fill one film canister with table salt.

5. Enlarge the class prediction graph, *Which one will melt first?,* and duplicate one marker for each student. Also copy one *fastest* and one *slowest* ribbon.

6. Make arrangements to use a freezer.

7. A camera can be used to keep a record of the changes that occur to the ice castles during the melting process. The pictures can serve as a reminder to the students when they discuss the activity.

Procedure

Part One

1. Invite the students to think about ice formations they see outside. Ask them if some of the ice melts faster than others. Then ask: Do you think all these ice cubes will melt in the same amount of time?

2. Give each group of students an ice cube in a pie tin. Tell them to look at the label on the bottom of the tin so that they will know which cube belongs to their group.

3. Ask the students to describe the shape of the ice. Ask them to compare the sizes of the cubes. (They should all be approximately the same size.) Discuss how long they think it will take for their cubes to melt if left in the pie tin in the classroom.

4. Record the time on the chalkboard. Have the students place their pie tins (with cubes) on a central table in the class until they are all melted.

5. Make a chart on the chalkboard with the starting time and a list of the labels (A, B, C, etc.) for the groups. When each cube completely melts, record that time next to its label on the chalkboard.

```
Start Time 9:00

Melt time
A    9:15
B    9:14
C    9:15
D    9:16
```

6. Discuss how long it took these cubes to melt. Ask them why they think the ice melted.

7. Challenge students to think whether the time would be any different if the ice had been a different size or shape, or placed somewhere else (next to a heater, outside, in a refrigerator, etc.). Ask them to explain their thinking.

Part Two

1. Review with the students details of the ice cubes melting. Cover such things as: The ice cubes all took *about* the same amount of time to melt. The ice cubes were all *about* the same size and shape. The ice cubes melted—turned to liquid—because they were warmed by the room's air. The ice changed from a solid to a liquid.

2. Gather the groups together with a different container for each group. Using the same letter identification as in *Part One,* have students write the letter of their group on a piece of masking tape and attach the tape to their container. Give each group an empty film canister and tell them they will use the canister as a measuring device. Invite them to fill the canister with water and pour it into their container.

3. Tell them to compare their container of water with those of other groups. Discuss what they observe. Ask leading questions such as: Is your container full? Does the water cover the bottom of the container? How high is the water in your container? What shape is the water in the container? Is there the same amount of water in each container? How do you know? [Yes, each one has one canister of water.]

4. Discuss how some containers appear full while others appear almost empty and why this happens.

5. Ask students to predict what shape the ice will be if they freeze the water in their containers. Ask them how they can get the water to change from a liquid to a solid. [Put it in the freezer. Put it outside (if the weather is cold enough).]

6. Place containers in the freezer (or outdoors) and allow time for the water to freeze—perhaps overnight.

7. After the water has frozen, help students remove the ice from the containers and place in their pie tins. Have them place the container beside the pie tin.

8. Record the time on the chalkboard. While the ice is melting, direct the students to closely observe the ice formations. Discuss and compare the sizes and shapes of the ice from each container.

9. Have students place a marker on the enlarged class graph to show their predictions as to which formation will melt first. Discuss how they made these choices.

10. Direct each group to draw a picture of their ice formation to show the shape and thickness. Tell them to label their picture with the letter (A, B, C, etc.) that corresponds to their container and to display these pictures next to the class graph.

11. As each ice formation finishes melting, direct the students to place ribbons on the class graph to indicate actual results of the *fastest* and the *slowest* melting ice formation.

12. Again discuss why the ice melted.

Part Three
1. Inform the students that they will be making ice castles and that they need to select three different containers in which their group will freeze some water to make the ice to build the castles.

2. Have them label the containers by writing their group letter on masking tape.

3. Direct them to again use the film canister as the measuring device and to pour one full canister of water into each container. Discuss what shape and thickness the ice will be for each container.

4. Freeze the water.

5. After the water has frozen, help students remove the ice from the containers. Distribute a canister of salt to each group.

6. Demonstrate how to join ice formations by lightly sprinkling salt on one surface of the ice. As soon as some liquid appears, place another piece of ice on top. The water will begin to freeze thus joining the two pieces.

7. Once all the castles have been built, discuss the new shapes that were formed. Discuss which shapes were easier to stack.

8. Record the time. Ask the students to predict how long it will take for the ice castles to melt. Have them explain their reasoning. Ask students to indicate which part(s) of the ice castles will melt the fastest. ...the slowest. Have them explain why.

9. Direct students to draw pictures of their ice castles. (To keep a record of the melting process, you may want to take photographs of the castles at various intervals.)

10. At regular intervals, return to the ice castles to observe the changes during the melting process. Discuss the changes, emphasizing the change in the state of matter—solid to liquid.

11. When the castles have all melted, compare the students' melting time predictions with the actual results. Have the students use vocabulary such as *greater than* and *less than*.

Discussion
1. What causes water to change to ice?
2. What causes ice to change to water?
3. What is ice?
4. What shape is water? Does its shape ever change? Explain.
5. Does the same amount of water look the same in all sizes and shapes of containers? Explain.
6. When water is frozen in a container, what shape is made? Explain.
7. Did all the ice formations take the same amount of time to melt? Which ones melted fastest? ...slowest? Why do you think some melted faster or slower than others?
8. Describe your ice castle.
9. What happened when you added salt to the ice formations?
10. If you didn't want your castle to melt so fast, what could you do to make it melt slower? [Put it in the freezer. Use a container that will give "thicker" ice.]
11. Tell some things you learned about ice.

Extensions
1. Have students bring containers from home that they want to use in building an ice castle. Use them to make one large castle for the entire class. To add color to the ice castles, use food coloring to tint film canisters filled with water. Demonstrate how to use a straw as a dropper by dipping one end into a canister of colored water. Once the straw is in the water, place one finger over the top of the straw. Pull the straw out of the water, hold it over the ice castle, and remove the finger from the top of the straw. This will release the water from the straw. Some of the colored water will freeze and some will simply run to the bottom of the structure.

2. Show the students pictures of icebergs. Discuss how these are very large pieces of ice found in nature. Begin a study of the Arctic regions. Study the adaptations made by humans and other animals to the severe climate conditions found there.

Home Link
Ask the students to observe the different shapes of ice formations made by nature around their homes. Do some melt faster than others? What do you notice about these shapes?

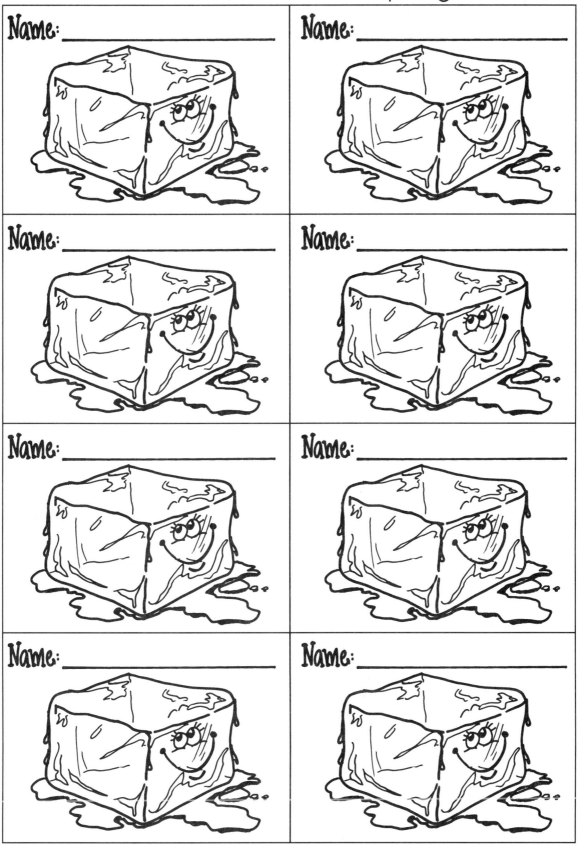

Name: _____

Name: _____

Name: _____

Name: _____

Name: _____

Name: _____

Name: _____

Name: _____

51

52

Frosty Forms

Part 1

1. Draw the shape of your ice.

2. How long do you think the ice will take to melt?

_____ minutes

3. How long did the ice take to melt?

_____ minutes

Part 2

1. Draw the shape of your ice.

2. How long do you think the ice will take to melt?

_____ minutes

3. How long did the ice take to melt?

_____ minutes

4. What shape melted fastest?
5. What shape melted slowest?

| fastest | slowest |

Ice Castles

1. Choose three containers.	**2.** Pour one canister of water in each.	**3.** Freeze and make ice.
4. Take ice out of containers.	**5.** Sprinkle a little salt on one piece of ice.	**6.** When liquid shows, put another piece of ice on top.

7.

"Draw your ice castle."

8. How long will it take for your ice castle to melt?

My prediction _____ Real Melting Time _____

FROSTY FORMS

Which one will melt first?

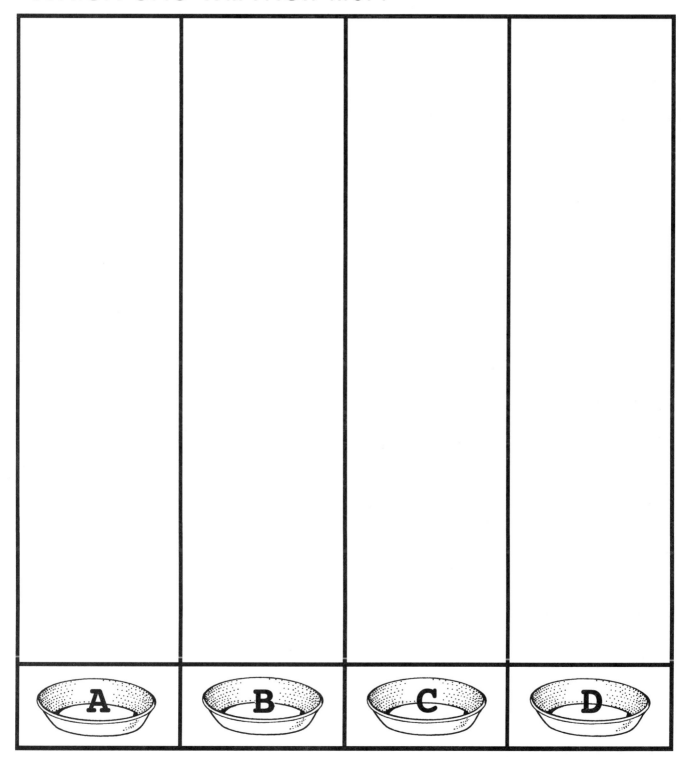

A	B	C	D

Room For Change

masking tape (see *Management 3*)
permanent marker (see *Management 3*)
access to water
Room for Change group recording journal

Topic
Changes in matter

Key Question
What changes can be observed when water freezes?

Focus
Students will discover that when a known quantity of water in the liquid state is frozen, its volume changes but its mass remains constant. They will also observe that water, as it changes from the liquid state to the solid state also changes in appearance.

Guiding Documents
Project 2061 Benchmarks
• *Things change in some ways and stay the same in some ways.*
• *Heating and cooling cause changes in the properties of materials.*

NRC Standard
• *Scientists develop explanations using observations (evidence) and what they already know about the world (scientific knowledge).*

NCTM Standards 2000*
• *Recognize the attributes of length, volume, weight, area, and time*
• *Compare and order objects according to these attributes*

Math
Measurement
    volume
    mass

Science
Physical science
    matter
        changes

Integrated Processes
Observing
Recording
Comparing and contrasting
Communicating

Materials
For each group of students:
    a balance (see *Management 1*)
    a unit of measure (see *Management 1*)
    two transparent film canisters (see *Management 2*)

For the class:
    freezer (see *Management 5*)
    chart paper

Background Information
This activity gives students an opportunity to practice their observational skills to see how water in the liquid state changes when frozen. The fact that water changes when it freezes is important to the survival of aquatic life in lakes and rivers. It is also important to us when we put a can of soda in the freezer just to cool, but we forget to take it out before it freezes.

Students will use a balance to directly compare the masses of two water-filled film canisters. The young learners will use either a set of noncustomary or customary units to quantify the mass of each of the canisters. They will discover that the mass of a water-filled film canister does not change when frozen.

The class will also observe the increase in volume as they see the ice rise above the top of the film canister. For your information, a film canister holds 35 mL of water. When frozen, the water will occupy a volume of approximately 38.5 mL. Volume is defined as the amount of space an object or matter occupies. Thus the volume is changed as the ice occupies more space than did the liquid water of the same mass.

The mass and volume of an object are single, physical properties of an object. An important physical property of an object is defined by the relationship between the mass of the object and its volume. This property is called *density*. Density is defined as the mass of an object divided by its volume.

Since the *volume* of the ice in container B is greater than the volume of the water in container A, the *density* of the ice is *less* than the density of the water. When either the volume or the mass of an object changes, the *density* will also simultaneously change.

Students at this level compare masses, observe volume changes and changes in appearance, but they are not yet ready to formally deal with the density concept. However, this activity is meant to offer an opportunity for students to observe the *effects* of the change in density that occurs when water freezes.

Ice floats in water because the density of ice is less than the density of water. This fact is the reason that lakes freeze from the top down instead of from the bottom up. If lakes froze from the bottom up, the ice would not melt during the summer months. That water above the ice would act as insulation. After a few years, lakes and rivers in the temperate zones around the Earth would be frozen solid all year round. The fish and other forms of aquatic life in these lakes and rivers would die.

Management

1. Each group will need a balance and a unit of measure such as 10 Teddy Bear Counters or gram masses to find the mass of their water and ice.

2. Collect two transparent plastic film canisters for each group. The black canisters will work, but the transparent canisters make the investigation more interesting as the students can see the water and ice as compared to the black canisters.

3. Provide one permanent marker and masking tape for each group to use to label their canisters. Each group will need a different colored marker to mark their canisters to distinguish them from the other groups' canisters.

4. For older students duplicate one recording journal per group.

5. Make arrangements to use the school freezer.

Procedure

Part One

1. Show the students two water-filled canisters. Ask them to discuss and predict what they think will happen to the water if one of the canisters is placed in the freezer for a couple of hours. Record their predictions on chart paper.

2. Invite the students to all participate in a science investigation to determine what they can observe about water that has been frozen in a canister. Give each group two film canisters, masking tape, a recording journal, and a marker.

3. Tell the students to place a piece of masking tape on each of their canisters. Ask each group to use a different colored marker to label their canisters to distinguish them from the other group's set of canisters. Tell them to mark one canister A and the other B.

4. Direct each group to completely fill both canisters with water. Ask them to describe the water in each container. [The water is clear. There is the same amount in each container and it is a liquid.]

5. Ask them to carefully compare the masses of the two canisters of water by placing one on one side of a balance and the other on the other side. The two canisters should balance each other. To quantify the measurement, tell the students to remove one canister and to replace it with a unit of measure such as Teddy Bear Counters, Unifix Cubes, or grams. Once they have determined the first canister's mass in units, tell

them to do the same for the second canister. (They should both be the same.) Direct them to record these measurements in their journal.

6. Discuss what the students observe about their group's two canisters of water. Record their observations on chart paper. [They look the same. They have the same mass.]

7. Introduce the vocabulary word, *volume*. Define volume to the students as the amount of space something takes up. Discuss how both canisters have the same volume because both canisters are the same shape and size. The volume of water in the two canisters is also the same because both canisters are filled to the top. The water is taking up the same amount of space in each canister, thus the two canisters of water have the same volume.

8. Challenge the students to predict what will happen to the water when placed in the freezer. Will the mass stay the same? Will the volume stay the same? Ask them to explain their thinking. Record their predictions on a class chart.

9. Direct each group to place their "B" canisters of water into the freezer and their "A" canisters of water in a safe place in the classroom. Leave the canisters undisturbed for two hours.

Part Two

1. After two hours, or once the B canisters of water are completely frozen, remove them from the freezer and give each group the appropriate canister.

2. Ask the students to compare their frozen canister of ice with their other canister that was not frozen. Discuss what the students observe. Record their comments on chart paper. [We made ice! It looks like the water got bigger when it froze. There is more ice than water. The ice goes over the top.]

3. Direct the students to use a balance to compare the mass of the two canisters. Discuss what they find out. Record their comments on chart paper. Tell them to record their measurements in their group journal.

4. Explain that the water increased in volume when it turned to ice, but that it stayed the same in mass. The volume of the water is changed as the ice occupies more space than did the liquid water of the same mass.

5. Discuss what the students have observed. Lead the discussion to bring out the following important elements of this activity. The water changed from a liquid to a solid, changed in appearance, got colder, and got bigger when frozen. A change in temperature made lots of changes to the water in canister B.

Part Three

1. Remind the students that their frozen canister and their canister of water have the same mass as was determined when they compared them using a balance. Remind them that the frozen water has more volume than the canister of liquid water. Discuss what the students think will happen when the ice in the frozen canister melts. Will the water take up the same amount of space as the ice? ...more? ...less? Will the water overflow the canister? Will the water be the same volume as they had before they froze the water? How will the melted ice canister compare to canister A that was never frozen? Ask them to predict what they think will happen when the ice melts. Ask them to explain why they think this. Record their predictions on chart paper.

2. Direct the students to place their canisters in a safe place where they will not be spilled until the ice completely melts.

4. At 10 minute intervals invite the class to check their canisters to see if the ice has completely melted. While the ice is melting, ask the students to notice that the ice that is not completely melted floats on top of the water. Discuss how ice cubes float when in a glass of water.

5. Discuss what the students have observed. Lead the discussion to bring out the following important elements of this activity. The ice changed from a solid to a liquid, changed in appearance, the water got warmer than the ice, and the ice got smaller as it melted back to water. A change in temperature made lots of changes to the ice in canister B.

Part Four

1. Once all the ice formations have melted, gather the groups together to observe and discuss the mass and volume of their canisters.

2. Tell the students to discuss what they observe about the volume of the water in canister B compared to the volume of the water in canister A. Direct them to find the mass of the water of the melted ice

using the balance and Teddy Bear Counters. Ask them to compare these measurements to the measurements taken before and after this canister was frozen. Discuss what the students have discovered. Did the change in temperature make a change in the mass of the water to ice? Did the change in temperature make a change in the volume of the water to ice?

Discussion

1. What did you notice about the water in the film canister compared to the ice in the frozen canister? [The ice was higher than the canister. It looked like there was more in the ice-filled canister than in the water-filled canister. The water and ice looked different—I couldn't see through it when it was ice. The water was a liquid and changed to a solid when frozen.]

2. What did you notice about the level of the ice in canister B compared to the water line before the water was frozen?

3. Explain what you think happens to water when it freezes. [It gets hard. It looks different. It gets bigger. It is cold.]

4. Explain how you measured the mass of the canisters.

5. Look at your journal. What do your measurements tell us about water that has been frozen and melted? [The mass stays the same.]

6. What did you notice about the ice while it was melting?

7. What happened to the volume of the water when it was frozen? [The volume got bigger.] What happened to the volume of the ice when it melted? [The volume got smaller.]

8. Describe what you think volume means.

Home Link

Ask the students to try the experiment at home using their ice trays or another shaped container.

* Reprinted with permission from *Principles and Standards for School Mathematics,* 2000 by the National Council of Teachers of Mathematics. All rights reserved.

I observed:

I discovered:

My science

Observation

Journal

by

59

Observe the two containers of water.

Predict what will happen if one is frozen.

Compare the two containers of water.

Find the mass of each container before freezing.

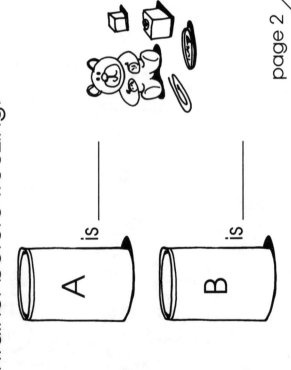

A ____ is ____

B ____ is ____

60

What happened after the water froze? Draw and write.

Compare the two containers.

A is ____

B frozen is ____

Mass

Volume color to show

Predict what will happen when the ice melts. Draw and write.

What happened when the ice melted? Draw and write.

Handmade Ice Cream

Topic
Changing matter: liquid to solid

Key Question
How does the ice cream mixture change?

Focus
Students will freeze ice cream and discover that the liquid ice cream mixture changes to a solid when it freezes.

Guiding Documents
Project 2061 Benchmarks
- *Things can be done to materials to change some of their properties, but not all materials respond the same way to what is done to them.*
- *Change is something that happens to many things.*

NRC Standards
- *Objects have many observable properties, including size, weight, shape, color, temperature, and the ability to react with other substances. Those properties can be measured using tools, such as rulers, balances, and thermometers.*
- *Materials can exist in different states—solid, liquid, and gas. Some common materials, such as water, can be changed from one state to another by heating or cooling.*

NCTM Standard 2000*
- *Use tools to measure*

Science
Physical science
   matter

Integrated Processes
Observing
Comparing and contrasting
Collecting and recording data
Drawing conclusions

Materials
For each student:
   plastic freezer bag, gallon size, zipper-type
   plastic freezer bag, pint size, zipper-type
   ice, crushed or small cubes
   salt
   plastic spoon

For the class:
   ice cream ingredients (See recipe card)
   measuring cup with handle, one-third cup
   newspaper
   paper towels
   mittens or gloves, optional

Background Information
When students are making ice cream, they can observe changes in matter from solid to liquid (ice to water) and liquid to solid (milk mixture to ice cream). As the ice melts, it absorbs energy. This energy comes from the liquid milk mixture since it is warmer than the ice. As this happens, the milk mixture cools because energy is being removed from it. When the milk mixture has had enough energy removed from it, it will turn to a frozen mixture (ice cream), changing from a liquid to a solid.

When the students freeze their ice cream mixture, they will put it into an ice/salt mixture that has a lower freezing point than ice. Because the salt and ice get colder than the freezing point of water (the main ingredient in the milk that is in ice cream), the ice cream will freeze. The students will be amazed because they will see the ice in the ice/salt mixture melting and think that it is getting warmer instead of colder.

Management
1. In this activity the students will take an ice cream mix and freeze it by flipping a freezer bag.
2. Each student will need a gallon-sized plastic bag, a pint-sized freezer bag, and a plastic spoon.
3. It is important that you use freezer-quality plastic bags to help prevent breaking while the students are flipping the bags to freeze the ice cream.
4. Using the *Ice Cream Recipe,* the ice cream mixture can be made beforehand and stored in the refrigerator until time to be used. It is best to keep the ingredients cold in order to speed the freezing process. One recipe is enough for 25-30 students if using slightly less than one-third cup of the mixture per student.
5. When students are ready to freeze the ice cream, have them put several layers of newspaper on the table surface to absorb the condensation that forms on the outside of the bag.

6. Put two or more small bags in the large gallon-size bag and let the students share the flipping chore.
7. **Be aware of students that have sugar and/or milk intolerances.** Have an alternative snack for these students when others are enjoying the ice cream they have made.

Procedure

1. Ask the students if they have ever made their own ice cream. Discuss what it takes to make ice cream—the various ingredients and ice.
2. Question them as to whether they think they could make ice cream without using an ice cream freezer or the freezer portion of a refrigerator.
3. Inform them that in this activity they will have to have temperatures cold enough to freeze water 32°F (0°C). Tell them that they will put ice into the gallon-sized freezer bag and add salt to make the temperature of the ice cream colder.
4. Instruct the students to fill the large plastic bag half full of ice and add $\frac{1}{4}$ cup of salt to the ice.
5. Prepare or have the ice cream mixture already prepared. Tell the students to place approximately $\frac{1}{3}$ cup of the ice cream mixture in their pint freezer bag and carefully seal the bag shut.
6. Instruct them to place the smaller bag inside the gallon bag with the salt and ice mixture, seal the larger bag, and start flipping it.
7. Tell the students that if they grab just the corners of the bag to flip it, their hands will not get uncomfortably cold. Use mittens or gloves, if necessary.
8. Ask the students to describe what is happening in the smaller bag as they are flipping the mixture. [It is becoming solid and freezing.]
9. When the freezing time is finished (approximately 10-15 minutes), check one bag to see if it is frozen. To do this, carefully remove it from the ice/salt, use a paper towel to thoroughly wipe the liquid from the zippered end of the bag (prevents salt water from contaminating the ice cream), and open the bag to see if the mixture is frozen. If it isn't, direct the students to continue flipping for a few more minutes.
10. When it is frozen, let everyone enjoy their frozen treat.

Discussion

1. What did you like best about this activity?
2. What made the ice cream freeze? When was it liquid? When was it solid?
3. Why did we use salt?
4. What would happen if you left the ice cream out of the refrigerator all night? Why?
5. Name some things you've seen change from liquid to solid. [water to ice cubes]

6. Name some things you have seen change from a solid to a liquid. [butter that melts]
7. How would you explain this experience of making ice cream to your parents?

Extensions

1. Make an extra sample bag of ice cream. Put a thermometer in the mixture in order to find the temperature of the ice cream before and after freezing. Also find the temperature of the ice/salt mixture.
2. Have the students try different recipes for the ice cream. Instead of vanilla pudding, have them try chocolate. They could also add real strawberries or peaches to the mixture.

Curriculum Correlation

Math:
1. Print the ice cream scoop pattern on white, pink, and brown construction paper. Using the ice cream pattern and cones, make a class graph of the students' favorite flavors.
2. Challenge the students to make as many different combinations of ice cream cones as they can.
3. Make pattern strips with flavors of ice cream. (Use the ice cream scoop pattern.)
4. Survey the whole school and make a school-wide graph of favorite flavors of ice cream. Put the graph in the hall or on the cafeteria wall.

Home Link

Send the recipe home so the parents can enjoy making ice cream with their children.

Handmade Ice Cream

...for 32 servings about $\frac{1}{3}$ cup each

Ice Cream Recipe

$2\frac{1}{2}$ cups sugar

1 can evaporated milk

2 teaspoons vanilla

1 package vanilla instant pudding

6 cups milk

salt
spoon
ice
plastic bags
gallon pint

1. Combine all the ingredients into a large bowl and mix until the sugar and pudding are dissolved.

2. Place $\frac{1}{3}$ cup of ice cream mixture into a small plastic bag. Seal the bag tightly.

3. Fill a large plastic bag full of ice. Add $\frac{1}{2}$ cup salt to the ice.

4. Put 1 or more small bags inside the large bag. Seal the bag tightly.

5. Grab the large bag by the corners and turn end over end for 10-15 minutes until frozen.

6. Open and eat!

Handmade Ice Cream Steps

1. Put newspaper on the desk. Get your bag. Shari

2. Wash your hands.

3. Put $\frac{1}{3}$ cup mixture in your bag. Shari Close the bag.

4. Put $\frac{1}{4}$ cup salt and $\frac{1}{2}$ bag of ice into large bag.

5. Put small bag inside big bag. Shari Close the bag.

6. Turn the bag over and over.

7. Take the small bag out. Shari Wipe it dry.

8. Open the bag. Eat ice cream.

WINTER WONDERS   65   © 2001 AIMS Education Foundation

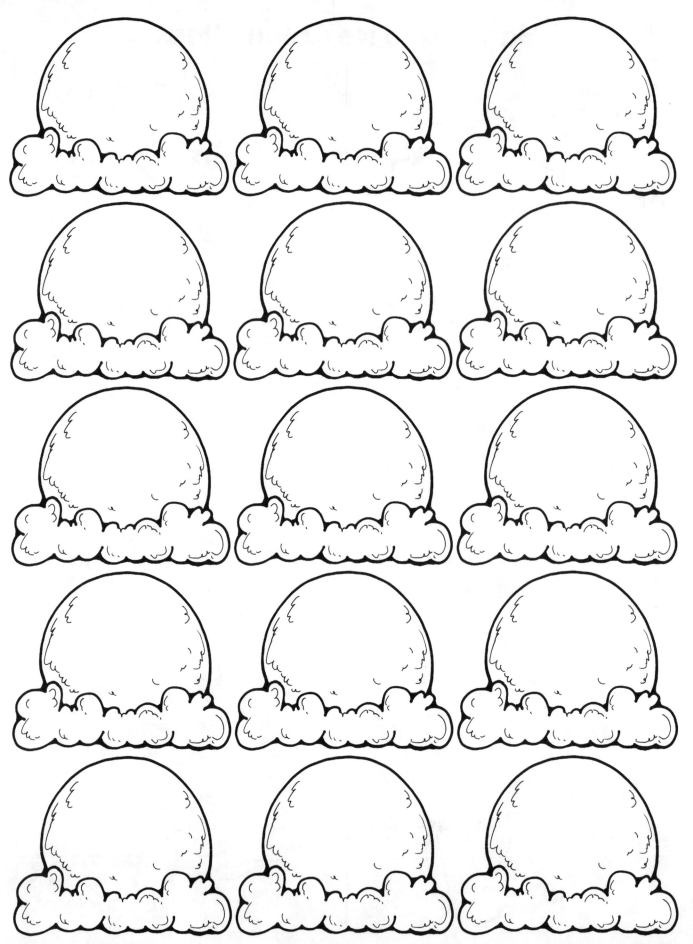

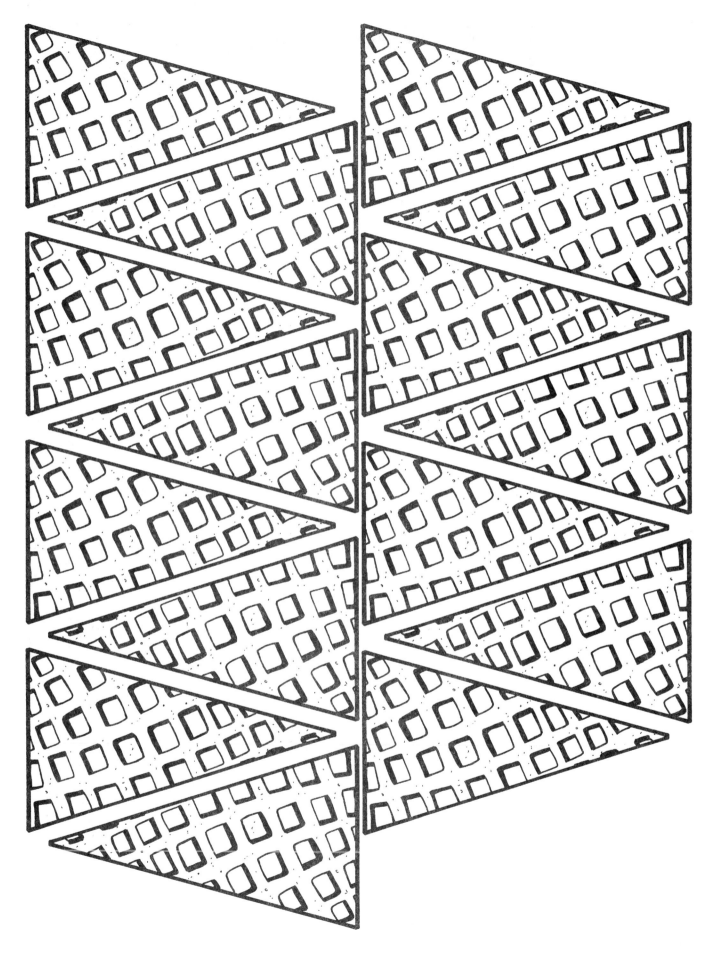

67

A Matter of Change

Topic
Matter

Key Question
What changes do you observe in the food we cook?

Focus
Using cooking experiences, students will investigate changes in matter when two or more substances interact to form new substances with different observable properties.

Guiding Documents
Project 2061 Benchmarks
- *Things change in some ways and stay the same in some ways.*
- *Things can change in different ways, such as in size, weight, color, and movement. Some small changes can be detected by taking measurements.*
- *Objects can be described in terms of the materials they are made of (clay, cloth, paper, etc.) and their physical properties (color, size, shape, weight, texture, flexibility, etc.).*
- *Things can be done to materials to change some of their properties, but not all materials respond the same way to what is done to them.*

NRC Standards
- *Objects have many observable properties, including size, weight, shape, color, temperature, and the ability to react with other substances, those properties can be measured using tools, such as rulers, balances, and thermometers.*
- *Materials can exist in different states—solid, liquid, and gas. Some common materials, such as water, can be changed from one state to another by heating or cooling.*

NCTM Standards 2000*
- *Understand how to measure using nonstandard and standard units*
- *Use tools to measure*
- *Select an appropriate unit and tool for the attribute being measured*

Math
Measurement
    mass
Number sense
    counting
    fractions

Science
Physical science
    matter

Integrated Processes
Observing
Recording
Comparing and contrasting
Communicating

Materials
For each student:
    recording sheets (see *Management 4*)

For each station:
    balance
    masses, customary or non-customary
    various ingredients and cooking supplies (see each recipe)
    recipe cards

Background Information
This investigation guides the young students through experiences in which they subject different foods to such treatments as heating, cooling, combining, and dissolving to see how they change. Throughout the cooking experiences, the students will make quantitative (measurement) and qualitative observations.

While many are familiar with the change of state between liquid water and ice, they may not understand that water exists as a gas when it evaporates; they may be likely to think that the water just disappears. Despite this simple idea, they can conduct investigations with heating, cooling, and combining different substances that help to develop inquiry skills and familiarize them with the idea that matter can exist in different states and that it can be changed from one state to another.

This lesson contains four experiences that show change. *The Toasted Cheese Square* and *Pie–In–A–Cup* change as a result of heating, the *Gelatin Cup* changes as a result of cooling, and *Sorda Pop* changes because of combining.

Management
1. Prior to this lesson, students should have experiences with identifying solid, liquid, and gaseous states of matter.
2. Each station is designed to be experienced separately and can be done on different days or weeks.
3. Duplicate one copy of each recipe card on card stock. Laminate for extended use. Place cooking station cards at the cooking station.
4. If developmentally appropriate, duplicate a recording sheet for each cooking experience. Students will record their observations of the ingredients before and after the cooking experience so they can determine that changes have occurred.
5. Before handling any food, remind students to thoroughly wash their hands.

Procedure

1. Review some of the properties of matter by asking the students what they know about things that are solid. ...liquid. ...gas.
2. Discuss how some things can change from a solid to a liquid, back to a solid, or to a gas. Ask the students to name some thing that make these kinds of changes. [water, ice, etc.] Record their suggestions on chart paper.
3. Ask the students to discuss what makes matter change. [heat, cold, combining it with other things]
4. Inform the children that they will be using food at the cooking station. They should observe several changes that happen because of different things they will be doing.
5. Demonstrate how to follow the directions on the *recipe cards* at the cooking station and how to use the recording sheets both *before* and *after* the cooking experience.
6. Upon completion, discuss the results with the class.

Discussion

1. Explain what you made today in the cooking station.
2. Describe what matter looked like—its shape, color, taste, and smell. Discuss its state—a solid, a liquid, or a gas.
3. What changes did you observe in your Toasted Cheese Square? What caused those changes? [heat]
4. What changes did you observe in your Gelatin Cups? What caused those changes? [cooling]
5. Describe whether the changes were slow or fast. Explain.
6. Look at your recording sheets, describe the things you made that were a liquid at first, then when heated or cooled changed to a solid. ...a solid first then when heated or cooled changed to a liquid.

7. Describe the things you made that changed more than one time during the preparation process. Explain.
8. Describe any changes that occurred without heating or cooling. [The Sorda Pop fizzled and tasted different.]
9. When you measured the mass before and after, were there any changes? Explain.
10. Name some other changes in matter you have observed at home. [Eggs change when you cook them. They make different changes depending on how you cook them, boiled, fried, or scrambled. Sugar and salt dissolve in water.]
11. Which cooking station did you like the best? ...the least? Explain why.

Home Links

1. To extend the lesson, send home the recording sheets for the students to experience the cooking lesson again with their families.
2. Ask the students to observe the preparation of food at home and to describe the changes that take place.
3. Direct the students to discuss the changes in matter they observed in class with their parents. Ask them to brainstorm together to list other changes in matter which they can observe around the home.

Curriculum Correlation

Other AIMS activities that help the young child build an understanding of matter can be found in *Sense-able Science.*

* Reprinted with permission from *Principles and Standards for School Mathematics,* 2000 by the National Council of Teachers of Mathematics. All rights reserved.

Cooking Stations

Toasted Cheese Squares

For each student:
one slice of bread
$\frac{1}{2}$ slice white cheese
$\frac{1}{2}$ slice yellow cheese
one small paper plate
one piece of aluminum foil
plastic knife

Materials at the station:
oven: convection, conventional, or toaster oven

Directions

1. Place the bread on the foil.
2. Use a knife to cut the cheese into strips or other shapes to make a design on the bread. Take a small taste of your Cheese Square snack before you cook it. Record on your recording sheet.
3. Look at your Cheese Square, smell it, touch it, then describe it on your recording sheet.
4. Using a balance, find the mass of your Cheese Square and record it.
5. Use the oven to melt the cheese. Cool.
6. Once again, look at your Cheese Square, smell it, touch it, then describe it on your recording sheet.
7. Using a balance, find the mass of your Cheese Square and record it on your sheet.
8. Taste your Cheese Square, compare this taste to your first taste. Record how you made your snack and what changes you observed.

Pie-In-A-Cup

For each student:
$\frac{1}{4}$ cup pumpkin pie mix
two teaspoons evaporated milk
$\frac{1}{2}$ orange (clean out the pulp leaving the shell)
one plastic spoon

Materials at each station:
one baking sheet
plastic knives
measuring cup, $\frac{1}{4}$ cup
one teaspoon
oven: convection or conventional

Directions

1. Measure pumpkin pie mix and place in the orange shell.
2. Add milk and stir.
3. Place on baking sheet. Take a small taste of your snack before you cook it.
4. Look at your snack, smell it, and touch it. Record on your recording sheet.
5. Using a balance, find the mass of your Pie-In-A-Cup and record it on your recording sheet.
6. Bake at 375 degrees for 10-12 minutes or until hot.
7. Remove from the oven and cool slightly. Find the mass of your Pie-In-A-Cup and record it on your recording sheet.
8. Look at your Pie-In-A-Cup, smell it, touch it, and taste it. Compare your cooked snack with the uncooked. Record how you made your Pie-In-A-Cup and what changes you observed.

Gelatin Cups

For each student:
one five-ounce cup
one tablespoon flavored gelatin mix
four tablespoons warm water
one plastic spoon

Materials at the station:
two tablespoons
refrigerator

Directions

1. Measure gelatin into cup.
2. Measure and stir warm water into cup. Stir until gelatin dissolves.
3. Look at your snack, smell it, touch it, and taste it. Record what you find out on your recording sheet.
4. Using a balance, find the mass of your Gelatin Cup and record it on your recording sheet.
5. Place in refrigerator for approximately 30 minutes or until solid.
6. Again look at it, smell it, and touch it, record on your recording sheet.
7. Find the mass of your Gelatin Cup and record it on your recording sheet.
8. Taste your Gelatin Cup, compare the taste, look, feel and smell of your gelatin to what it was before. Record how you made your gelatin and what changes you observed.

Sorda Pop

For each student:
one nine-ounce cup
one cup of fruit juice
$\frac{1}{8}$ teaspoon baking soda

Materials at the station:
$\frac{1}{8}$ teaspoon
measuring cup, one cup size

Directions

1. Measure fruit juice into a cup. Take a small taste of the juice.
2. Record how the juice looks, smells, feels, and tastes.
3. Measure baking soda into the cup of juice. Stir well.
4. While the juice is still fizzing, use a balance to find the mass of your Sorda Pop and record it on your recording sheet.
5. Wait for the juice to stop fizzing and measure the mass of your Sorda Pop and record on your recording sheet. Record also how your Sorda Pop looks, smells, and feels.
6. Taste your Sorda Pop, compare its taste, appearance, smell, and feel to that of the juice it was before. Record how you made your snack and what changes you observed.

Before

Toasted Cheese Squares Observations

After

Before

Matter ✏

Look	Smell
Touch	**Taste**
Mass	

After

Matter ✏

Look	Smell
Touch	**Taste**

Pie in a Cup Observations

Before

Matter ✏️

Look	Smell
Touch	Taste
Mass 🚗	

After

Matter ✏️

Look	Smell
Touch	Taste

Before **After**

Gelatin Cups Observations

Before

Matter ✏

Look

Smell

Touch

Taste

Mass

After

Matter ✏

Look

Smell

Touch

Taste

Before

Sorda Pop Observations

After

Matter ✏		
Look	Smell	
Touch	Taste	
Mass		

Matter ✏		
Look	Smell	
Touch	Taste	

Wash
your hands.

All stations

Find the mass.

All stations

Record

Write and draw your observations.

I see

All stations

Lay the bread on the foil.

Toasted Cheese Squares

Slice the cheese.

Then make a design.

Toasted Cheese Squares

Toast the cheese square.

Toasted Cheese Squares

Put $\frac{1}{4}$ cup of pumpkin pie mix in an orange.

Pie-In-A-Cup

Mix in 2 teaspoons of evaporated milk.

Pie-In-A-Cup

Bake until hot.

Pie-In-A-Cup

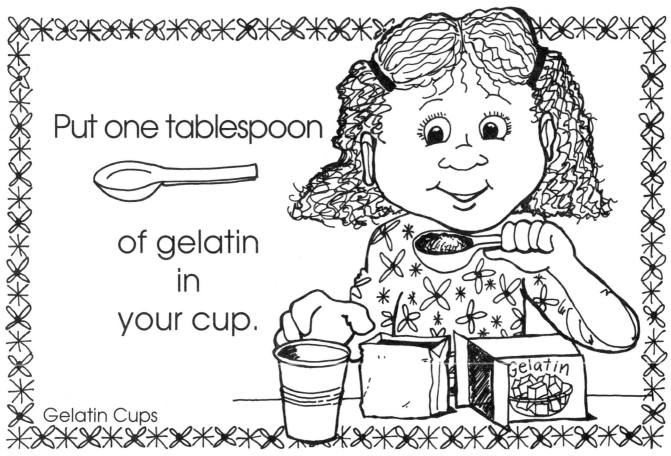

Put one tablespoon

of gelatin
in
your cup.

Gelatin Cups

Stir in
4 tablespoons
of hot water.

Gelatin Cups

Place in
refrigerator.

Gelatin Cups

Pour one cup of fruit juice in the cup.

Sorda Pop

Put $\frac{1}{8}$ teaspoon baking soda into the juice.

Sorda Pop

BAKING SODA

Temperature Told 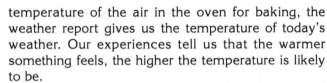 Hot or Cold

Topic
Thermometers

Key Question
How does a thermometer help us?

Focus
Students learn about a thermometer by building a model as well as by using an immersion thermometer.

Guiding Documents
Project 2061 Benchmark
• *A model of something is different from the real thing but can be used to learn something about the real thing.*

NRC Standard
• *Objects have many observable properties, including size, weight, shape, color, temperature, and the ability to react with other substances. Those properties can be measured using tools, such as rulers, balances, and thermometers.*

Math
Measurement

Science
Physical science
  temperature

Integrated Processes
Observing
Communicating
Comparing and contrasting

Materials
For each student:
  thermometer
  strip of red construction paper
  glue stick

For each pair of students:
  immersion thermometer
  one transparent cup of ice or snow
  one transparent cup of very warm water

Background Information
Heat and temperature are related, but they are not the same thing. Most people are familiar with the idea of temperature. The temperature of our bodies is important for our health, recipes tell us the

temperature of the air in the oven for baking, the weather report gives us the temperature of today's weather. Our experiences tell us that the warmer something feels, the higher the temperature is likely to be.

A thermometer is an instrument used for measuring temperature, usually by expansion or contraction of mercury or alcohol in a tube and bulb. CAUTION: Use only alcohol thermometers when working with young students.

Heat energy flows from warmer to cooler. If two objects are put into contact, and we wait until all changes stop, the objects will be at the same temperature. If we put the end of a thermometer into something hot, heat energy will flow from the substance to the thermometer and it will come to the same temperature as the substance. No matter where we put the thermometer, the energy will flow in or out and make the thermometer the same temperature as the substance it touches.

Management
1. Immersion thermometers can be purchased from AIMS. Those thermometers that have a V-shape structure are more durable for use with young students.
2. It is best to do this activity with partners so thermometers can be shared. Each student should make a model of the thermometer and make his or her own predictions in the activity.
3. Prepare the red construction paper strips for the thermometer models ahead of time by cutting 3" x 11" strips.
4. Caution students not to rapidly move their thermometers from a substance of one temperature to something with a radically different temperature. They should wait a few minutes before immersing the thermometer into the new substance.
5. A large class thermometer can be made by enlarging the activity sheet of the thermometer and cutting a long piece of red paper to slip into the sleeve. The teacher can then use this as a model while students are making and discussing their predictions.
6. This activity begins with the review of the terms *hot* and *cold*. The students will discuss various items that are either hot or cold and place the pictures under the correct headings.
7. The students then will dramatize the movement of the red column in a thermometer so that they can observe and relate to the changes in models

and actual thermometers. It is important to go back and forth from the model to the actual thermometer as described in *Procedure* as well as using the dramatization. The dramatization is repeated during the activity to reinforce the movement of the actual column of liquid in a thermometer. These diverse experiences are a way of getting understanding for the various learning styles in the classroom.

Procedure

1. Review the terms *hot* and *cold*. Discuss the pictures at the bottom of the recording sheet *Temperature Told*. Ask the students how they know each item is hot or cold. Have them relate their experiences with each item. Direct the students to cut out the pictures and paste them in the correct box.

2. Hold up a thermometer or the enlarged thermometer (see *Management 5)* and ask the students how this tool helps them learn about things. Point to the red column on the thermometer and ask them what that column tells them, what happens to it, and why. Read *Temperature and You* (see *Curriculum Correlation).*

3. Have the students make their thermometer headbands as directed on the activity sheet. Once they are done, have them put the headbands on and act out changes in temperature. For example: Direct students to squat down and tell them it is very cold, so cold it may snow. Then describe the sun coming up and the air warming. Ask them what should happen to the thermometer's red column (their headbands). [The red column moves up.] Continue with other scenarios of changes in temperature as the students, dressed in their thermometer headbands, act out the changes by raising and lowering their bodies.

4. Demonstrate how to make the model of the student thermometer.

5. Once students have made their models, lead them in a discussion which will connect the dramatization they did with the model of a thermometer they just made. Focus their attention on what happens to the red column in each case.

6. Hold up an immersion thermometer and show the students how to properly use it. Talk about the glass portion and how it can break if misused. Tell the students they are going to be using the thermometer as a tool to learn about the temperature of things. Caution them not to move the thermometer from hot things to cold things too quickly.

7. Distribute a transparent plastic cup with ice or snow in it. Ask the students

to predict what will happen to the red column in the immersion thermometer when they put it into the ice. Have the students show their predictions first with their body position (upright or squatting) and then with their model thermometers. Once they have predicted with their models (adjusted red column), say "everybody show" at which time all students should hold up their thermometers so you can scan the group.

8. Distribute the immersion thermometers (one to each pair of students), and then direct them to carefully immerse them into the ice and observe what happens. (They should watch it for at least three minutes to allow it to stabilize.) After observing the changes in the red column, they should adjust the red column in their models to match what has happened to the real thermometer. Again, say "everybody show" and scan the group to access their understanding of the changes in the thermometer.

9. Have students remove the thermometers from the ice and allow time for the thermometers to stabilize to room temperature. Repeat the procedure using very warm water, predicting with their bodies and the models, using the real thermometers, and then adjusting the models.

10. Discuss what they learned and how they can use this skill of reading a thermometer.

Discussion

1. How did the red line change when it was in ice? ...very warm water?
2. What would the red line look like if you put it in your snowman? ...Dad's coffee?
3. Where have you seen thermometers before?
4. Why are thermometers important?

Extensions

1. Use the immersion thermometer in other things like lukewarm water, sand, or soil.
2. Apply this understanding to the use of an indoor/outdoor thermometer.

Curriculum Correlation

1. Read: Maestro, Betsy and Giulio. *Temperature and You.* Lodestar Books. New York. 1990.
2. Describe the changes in temperature when writing in your journal.
3. Sing the song *Just Right.*

Home Link

1. Have students take their model thermometers home and explain them to their parents.
2. Encourage students to find thermometers around their house and start using them to find out about the changes in the temperature.

83   © 2001 AIMS Education Foundation

Temperature Told **Hot** or **Cold**

☀ **Hot**	❄ **Cold**

ice cream	stove	cocoa	ice water	ice cream bar
soup	freezer	candle flame	snow	fire

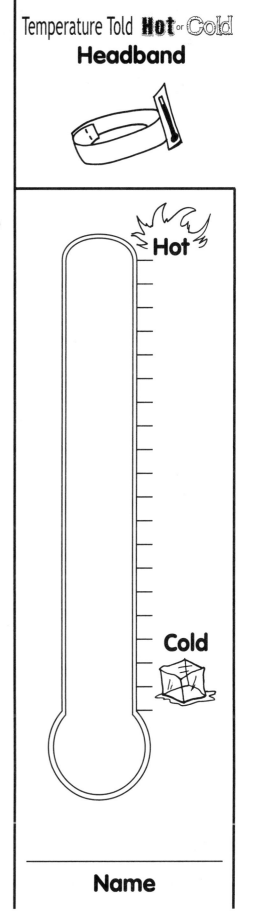

Temperature Told Hot or Cold
Headband

Hot

Cold

_____
Name

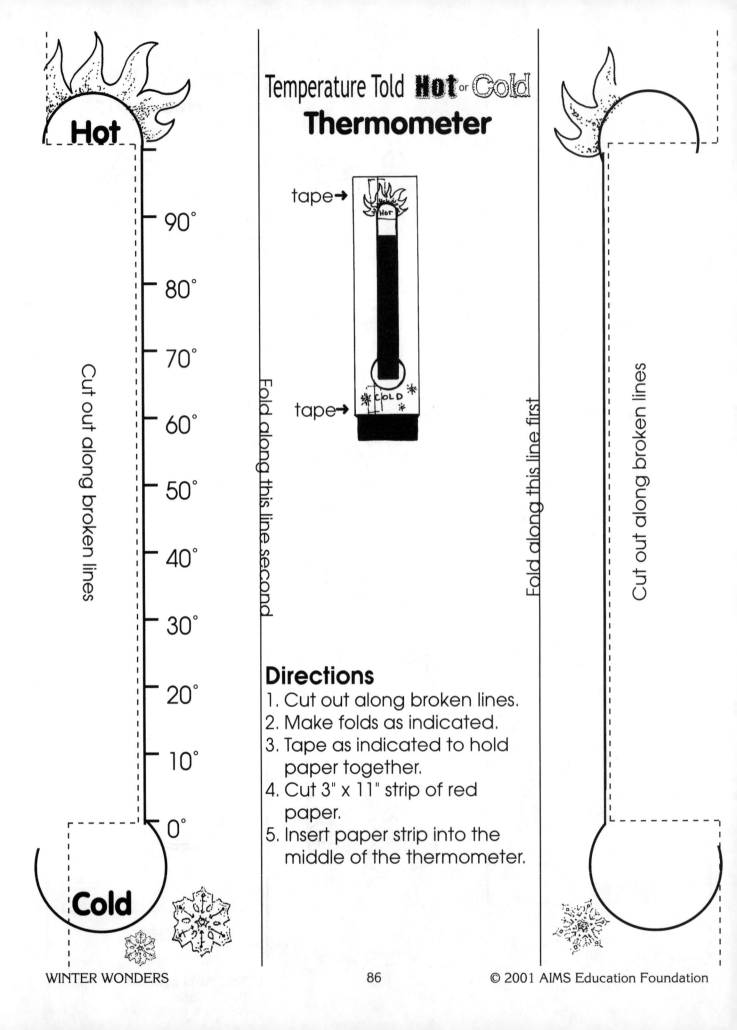

Temperature Told **Hot** or **Cold**
Thermometer

Hot

90°
80°
70°
60°
50°
40°
30°
20°
10°
0°

Cut out along broken lines

Cold

Fold along this line second

tape→

tape→

Fold along this line first

Cut out along broken lines

Directions
1. Cut out along broken lines.
2. Make folds as indicated.
3. Tape as indicated to hold paper together.
4. Cut 3" x 11" strip of red paper.
5. Insert paper strip into the middle of the thermometer.

Just Right

Words by Suzy Gazlay

Tune: Polly Wolly Doodle

My mom cooks por-ridge just for me And it real-ly makes me glad; If it's too hot I burn my tongue; Too cold, it sure tastes bad. When it's right, it's just right, And it sure is fine with me; Yes, when the tem-per-a-ture's just right, I'm hap-py as can be!

Optional Verses

When I play hard and need a drink
Cold milk sure hits the spot;
If it's too cold, though, it might freeze,
Or spoil if it's too hot. (chorus)

In summer if it gets too hot
I just don't want to play;
But sometimes it might be so cold
that I can't swim all day. (chorus)

In winter if it gets too hot,
There's rain instead of snow;
But sometimes I must stay inside
While icy cold winds blow. (chorus)

Hand motions may be used to accompany this song. Have the children pretend that they are thermometer. Whenever something too hot is mentioned, they should reach up high; when they sing about something too cold, they should reach down low. At the just right parts, they should make sweeping motions with their hands at their sides. Add other familiar motions as you wish.

Weather Wear

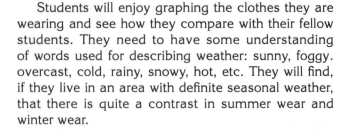

Topic
How weather affects what we wear

Key Questions
What are you wearing today? What is the weather like today?

Focus
Students will learn that weather influences what they wear.

Guiding Document
Project 2061 Benchmarks
- *Simple graphs can help to tell about observations.*
- *Different people may make different choices for different reasons.*

Math
Graphing

Science
Weather

Integrated Processes
Observing
Comparing and contrasting
Communicating
Collecting and recording data
Interpreting data
Applying

Materials
12" x 18" construction paper, for two-circle Venn diagrams
Glue
Scissors
Pictures of clothes the students might wear
Pictures of weather
Sticky notes, $1\frac{1}{2}$ x 2 inches
Bar graph, made on bulletin board

Background Information
Humans wear clothing for protection and decoration. Students many times do not know that what they wear is so often influenced by the weather. They just know that when it is warm, they are uncomfortable in their winter clothes, and when it is cold they want to wear more than they did in the summer.

Students will enjoy graphing the clothes they are wearing and see how they compare with their fellow students. They need to have some understanding of words used for describing weather: sunny, foggy. overcast, cold, rainy, snowy, hot, etc. They will find, if they live in an area with definite seasonal weather, that there is quite a contrast in summer wear and winter wear.

Management
1. This is an activity that can be done with the whole class or in small groups.
2. You may want to change some of the categories listed on the graph to fit your climate.
3. Prepare the graph on the bulletin board. Suggested size, 24 x 36 inches.
4. For the Venn diagram, draw two overlapping circles on the construction paper.
5. Make enough copies of the pictures of the clothes so each child will be able to have a set.
6. If there isn't a picture that fits what a child is wearing, give him or her a blank piece of paper on which to sketch the clothes.

Procedure
1. Talk about today's weather and what kind of clothes the students are wearing. Ask the students why they or their parents picked the outfits they have on.
2. Discuss how the weather influences what the students wear for the day. For example, if it is raining or snowing, they would probably wear protective clothing.
3. Discuss each of the pictures shown on the worksheet. For example, "jeans and a T-shirt" may also represent "a blouse and slacks." Have the students think about which pictures apply to them.
4. Have the students describe the weather and record it on the graph.

Sorting
1. Tell the students to look carefully at all the pictures of the clothes.
2. Ask them to pick out all the clothes that they might wear in the winter. ...spring. ...summer. ...fall.
3. Ask the students to explain why they wear those certain clothes during those seasons.

4. Sort by placing the pictures in a two-circle Venn diagram. For example: In one circle they would place "Things I wear in the summer," in the other circle they would place "Things I wear in the winter." Ask the students to explain the clothes in the overlapping set?

Weather Wear Recording Sheet
1. Discuss what the weather is like on that day and tell them to mark on the recording sheet by circling the temperature (hot, warm, cool, cold) and gluing on the weather symbols to match.
2. Instruct the students to look at all the pictures on the sheet. If any item of clothing they are wearing does not appear on the sheet, tell them to draw the item(s) on $1\frac{1}{2}$ x 2 sticky notes.
3. Tell them to take the pictures of clothing they are wearing and glue them on the recording sheet.
4. Ask the students to tell why they wore those clothes to school today. Ask them to explain if the weather had any influence on their choice.
5. Have them compare their choices of clothing with their neighbors. Are they the same or different? Ask them to explain.

What Are You Wearing Today?
1. Suggest the students use their *Weather Wear* recording sheet as a reference to illustrate the child on the page *What Are You Wearing Today?* Instruct them to record the day's weather word description (warm, cold, rainy, etc.)
2. Have the students compare their illustrations with their neighbor's recording sheet. Are the pieces of clothing the same or different? Let the students explain their choices.
3. Use the illustration on *What Are You Wearing Today?* to make a graph. Let the students decided what discrete categories they would like to graph, (e.g., wearing a sweater or short sleeves; wearing boots or sandals or tie shoes; etc.). Put the graph on the bulletin board, and discuss why they chose these clothes to graph.
4. Graph several times, using different categories each time.

Discussion
1. What is the weather like today?
2. How does the weather influence what we wear?
3. What are some other factors besides weather that may influence what we wear?
4. If we did this activity again next week (or next month, in June, or at Thanksgiving) would your recording sheet look the same? Which categories might be the same? Which would be different?

5. Explain your Venn diagram.
6. Describe how you illustrated the child on the activity sheet.

Extensions
1. Save one of the graphs and do the same activity at a different time of the year. Compare graphs.
2. Do this activity at the beginning of each season and compare.
3. Try covering the weather section of a graph done earlier in the year and see if the class can use the information on the graph to determine what the weather was like on that day.
4. Use the blank graph and have the students record the weather for a week at time, gluing the weather symbols in the days. They can save the sheet and do the same during a week in each of the three other seasons of the year. Then let them compare the weather in the different seasons.

Curriculum Coordinates
Language Arts:
1. Read Aesop's fable "The Wind and the Sun."
2. Have the students think of clothing that would be appropriate for different types of weather (mittens, sundress, raincoat, for example). List these words on charts for experience stories or on word cards for categorizing activities.

Social Studies:
Find out how people of other cultures dress for weather similar to the weather in your area.

Clothing Samples

closed shoes	open shoes	boots	socks tights
shirt	dress	swimsuit	mittens gloves
shirt	skirt	coat	raincoat umbrella
T-shirt	pants	jacket	earmuffs scarf cap
T-shirt	jeans	sweat shirt	hat cap
T-shirt	shorts	sweater	overalls

Weather Symbols - Weather Wear

foggy	foggy	foggy	foggy
windy	windy	windy	windy
snowy	snowy	snowy	snowy
rainy	rainy	rainy	rainy
cloudy	cloudy	cloudy	cloudy
sunny	sunny	sunny	sunny

Weather Wear

Name: _____   Season: _____

What is the weather like today?

Hot   Warm

Cool   Cold

What clothing did you wear today?

Why did you wear these clothes today?

Weather Wear

Name: _____ Weather: _____

What are you wearing today?

Draw your hair, face,
and clothes to look
just like you today. Draw
in today's weather

What is the Weather?

☀ Summer   🍂 Fall   ⛄ Winter   🌼 Spring

Friday				
Thursday				
Wednesday				
Tuesday				
Monday				

Counting on 100

Topic
Exploring the number 100.

Key Question
What can you do in 100 seconds?
(See specific activities for other *Key Questions*)

Focus
Students will perform various activities in their quest for 100.

Guiding Documents
Project 2061 Benchmarks
- *Numbers can be used to count things, place them in order, or name them.*
- *Patterns can be made by putting different shapes together or taking them apart.*

NCTM Standards 2000*
- *Select an appropriate unit and tool for the attribute being measured*
- *Understand how to measure using nonstandard and standard units*
- *Use tools to measure*

Math
Skip counting (tens, fives, ones)
Grouping sets of 10
Measurement
    linear
    mass
    time
    volume
Logical reasoning
Problem solving
Estimating

Integrated Processes
Observing
Collecting and recording data
Comparing and contrasting

Materials
(See each activity for specific materials)
Clock with a second hand

Background Information

Counting to 100 helps young students make connections between relationships of smaller numbers and similar relationships of larger numbers. In the activities provided, students can count by ones, fives, and tens to 100. They can do other activities to find the mass and volume of 100 objects. Not only are students asked to count, but they are also asked to record the numerals that represent their counts.

For many traditional primary grades, the 100th day of school falls somewhere in the month of February. These varied experiences can be used to reinforce the concept of 100 as part of a celebration of that day.

Management
1. The teacher can select any number of the provided activities for reinforcing the concept of 100.
2. These activities can be done at centers or as a whole class, over an entire day or interspersed over several days.
3. It is urged that time for discussion be given at the end of each activity. During this time students should compare and contrast results and make inferences as to why variations may occur.
4. Prescribed discussion questions are not provided because the selection and sequence of activities is left to the teacher.
5. It is also urged that various methods of recording and displaying data be used. Student journals, tallies, representational graphs, and abstract graphs such as bar graphs are some suggestions.
6. Be sure to have an ample number of activity pages because some students may finish more than one page in 100 seconds. To conserve copying paper, use the front and back of each sheet.

Procedure
1. Several of the activities require students to perform tasks in 100 seconds. To establish the concept of 100 seconds prior to performing the other tasks, direct the students' attention to a clock with a second hand. Starting at the 12, show the students the path the second hand travels to equal 100 seconds. (For consistency purposes, it is suggested that timing always begin at the 12.)
2. Follow the procedure for each of the other selected activities.
3. Use *My Book of 100* as recording sheets. Cut the sections apart and staple the left side to make a book for the students to take home.

Discussion
Questions will vary depending upon activities that were selected.

Culminating Activity
Host a collection day. Have all the students collect 100 objects (pebbles, beads, pennies, buttons, leaves, seeds, stamps, etc.). On *Celebrating 100 Day* have all children bring their collections to school to share.

Do these activities with the students to present their collections.
- Ask the students why they chose to collect what they did?
- Play 20 questions to guess the items collected.
- Make a 100 museum and display their collections.
- How many items are there in all?

Curriculum Correlation
Literature

Cuyler, Margery. *100th Day Worries*. Simon & Schuster Books for Young Readers. New York. 2000.

Harris, Trudy. *100 Days of School*. The Millbrook Press. Brookfield, CT. 1999.

Medearis, Angelo Shelf. *The 100th Day of School*. Scholastic Press. New York. 1996.

Slate, Joseph. *Miss Bindergarten Celebrates the 100th Day*. Dutton Children's Books. New York. 1998.

Wells, Rosemary. *Emily's First 100 Days of School*. Hyperion Books for Children. New York. 2000.

* Reprinted with permission from *Principles and Standards for School Mathematics*, 2000 by the National Council of Teachers of Mathematics. All rights reserved.

I found things that were 100 ♥hearts long.

Name _____

My Book of 100T

I built a tower in 100 seconds with ___ blocks.

It was ___ ♥hearts tall.

I cut out ♥hearts for 100 seconds.

I cut out ___ ♥hearts.

I used a _____.

I colored _____ s in 100 seconds.

I balanced 100 _____ s with these.

I circled _____ sets of 10 ♥s in 100 seconds.

I circled _____ sets of 10 ★s in 100 seconds.

I filled a cup with 100 of these.

99

Coloring Rabbits

Key Question: How many rabbits can you color in 100 seconds?

Materials: crayons, activity page of rabbits, clock

Procedure:

1. Tell the students they will have 100 seconds to color as many rabbits as they can.
2. Distribute activity page and crayons.
3. Wait for the clock's second hand to reach the 12, then tell the students to begin coloring.
4. At the end of 100 seconds, direct the students to ring groups of 10 rabbits and count their results.
5. Have them record the number of rabbits colored on their paper or in their student journals. You may want to make a class graph to show the combined results.

Circling Hearts and Stars

Key Question: How many sets of 10 hearts can you circle in 100 seconds?

Materials: crayon, hearts and stars activity pages, clock

Procedure:

1. Tell students they will have 100 seconds to circle as many sets of 10 hearts as they can.
2. Demonstrate how students may want to count 10 hearts and circle them. Strategies may include writing numbers beside the hearts or making a mark on each heart as it is counted.
3. At the end of 100 seconds, direct the students to record the number of hearts they circled.
4. Using this round as a point of reference, ask the students to predict how many stars they will be able to circle in 100 seconds.

Building Towers

Key Question: How tall a tower can you build in 100 seconds?

Materials: wooden blocks, tape measures, clock

Procedure:

1. Tell students that their group (2-4 members) will have 100 seconds to build a block tower as high as they can.
2. Distribute a large collection of wooden blocks to each group.
3. Wait for the clock's second hand to reach the 12, then tell the students to begin building.
4. At the end of 100 seconds, direct the students to stop building and measure the height of their towers. Instruct them to record their results in their student journals.
5. Have students predict whether or not they could build a taller structure if they repeated this activity. Repeat the activity.

Cutting Hearts

Key Question: How many hearts can you cut out in 100 seconds?

Materials: scissors, a minimum of 20 3" x 3" squares of red, pink, and white paper for each student, clock

Procedure:

1. Tell students they will have 100 seconds to cut out as many paper hearts as they can, one at a time.
2. Distribute the scissors and paper squares to each student.
3. Demonstrate how to fold a square piece of paper in half and to cut the heart starting at the fold. (Some students may first want to draw the shape on the paper.)
4. Wait for the clock's second hand to reach the 12, then tell the students to begin cutting.
5. At the end of 100 seconds, direct the students to count their cutout hearts and record the results on a class graph or in student journals.

100

Heart Measuring Tape

Key Question: What can you find that is 100 hearts long?

Materials: glue or tape, scissors, measuring tape handout

Procedure:

1. Have students make a heart measuring tape by cutting and taping the heart strips.
2. Have students number the hearts from one to 100.
3. Tell them that they will work in groups of four to find objects that are 100 hearts in length.
4. Have students illustrate or label the objects they found in their student journals.
5. Allow at least 20-30 minutes of time for students to complete this activity.

100 Friendly Bears

Key Question: What can you find that has the same mass as 100 Friendly Bears? (For more advanced students, you may want to use 100 grams.)

Materials: balance, Friendly Bears, baby food jars filled with various items

Procedure:

1. At a center set out a balance, Friendly Bears, and five baby food jars filled with various items.
2. Have students count out 100 Friendly Bears and place them in one pan of the balance.
3. Instruct the students to find objects that have the same mass as the Friendly Bears. (They can use the jars as part of this mass.)
4. Direct the students to record their results in their student journals.
5. Extend this activity to objects that the students can find around the room.

100 Pattern Blocks

Key Question: What kind of geometric design can you make with 100 pattern blocks?

Materials: *For each group of four students:* 100 pattern blocks, paper cutouts of pattern block shapes, 12" x 18" sheet of black construction paper

Procedure:

1. Distribute pattern blocks to student groups. Instruct them to use all 100 blocks in a geometric design of their choice.
2. When the design is completed, have students duplicate it by gluing the paper cutouts onto black construction paper.
3. Have groups compare and contrast their designs with others. (symmetry, size, etc.)
4. Display finished papers on the bulletin

Fill The Cup

Key Question: What 100 objects can you find to fill a 5-oz. cup?

Materials: 5-oz. cup, variety of objects in zippered plastic bags (lima beans, pinto beans, rice, macaroni, beads, etc.)

Procedure:

1. Direct the students to predict which 100 objects will fill the 5-oz. cup.
2. Instruct the students to arrange the bags in order from most likely to least likely to have 100 fill the cup.
3. Have students count 100 objects from each bag and test by pouring them into the 5-oz. cup.
4. Have students record their results in their student journals.
5. Alter the rules of the game and have the students find containers that would be filled by 100 objects from each choice of items.

103

104

BIRTHDAY CELEBRATIONS

Topic
Integrated unit applying measurement, data collection, number, and pattern

Key Question
What math is there in a birthday celebration?

Focus
Students will apply basic skills in measurement, data collection, number, and pattern through a theme.

Guiding Document
NCTM Standards 2000*
- *Understand how to measure using nonstandard and standard units*
- *Use tools to measure*
- *Sort and classify objects according to their attributes and organize data about the objects*
- *Develop understanding of the relative position and magnitude of whole numbers and of ordinal and cardinal numbers and their connections*
- *Develop a sense of whole numbers and represent and use them in flexible ways, including relating, composing, and decomposing numbers*
- *Pose questions and gather data about themselves and their surroundings*
- *Recognize and apply mathematics in contexts outside of mathematics*

Math
Measurement
  length
Numbers
Patterns

Science
Physical science
  matter

Integrated Processes
Observing
Comparing and contrasting
Communicating
Collecting and recording data
Applying

Materials
For each group of four students:
  set of candles (see *Management 2*)
  chart paper
  markers or crayons
  shoelaces (see *Management 3*)
  one wrapped present (see *Management 3*)
  measuring tool (see *Management 4*)
  a balloon
  tablespoon
  Unifix cubes

For each student:
  5-oz waxed paper cup (see *Management 6*)
  one craft stick
  a party hat in the shape of a cone
  a journal or activity sheets

For the class:
  electric skillet
  cake mix (see *Management 5*)
  a literature book with a party theme (see *Curriculum Correlation*)

Background Information
   Winter is a time when we celebrate the birthdays of Abraham Lincoln, George Washington, Martin Luther King, and several other famous people, making it appropriate that an activity on birthdays be included in this book.

   This birthday celebration can center around a president's birthday or another significant event. It is designed to give the students an opportunity to apply basic skills, which have been previously learned, in an exciting format.

   The activity offers explorations in math; however, additional social studies, language arts, science, P.E., art, music, and drama activities could easily be added to completely integrate the lesson.

Management
1. If you teach this activity utilizing stations, you will only need one set of materials, which can be used over and over again. Have the students work in groups of four at the station.

2. Gather an assortment of candles typically used on birthday cakes. Store them in a recloseable bag. Each group of four students will need:
   - two candles that are the same length but of different colors,
   - six to ten others that are all different colors,
   - six to ten others in an assortment of colors that are all different in length from one another.
3. Gather an assortment of shoelaces. Each group of four students will need:
   - two laces that are the same length but of different colors,
   - four to six others in an assortment of colors that are all different in length from one another.

   Place the laces for each group in a box and wrap it with colorful paper and place a bow on top. Try to find a variety of sizes of bows to use on the packages. (Socks can be used instead of laces.)
4. Provide a measuring tool for each group, either a 30-centimeter ruler, a 12-inch ruler, or a standard unit measuring tape, straw ruler, etc.
5. Purchase a cake mix which only calls for the addition of water. Most mixes are large enough that one box will be sufficient for the entire class. Set up a cooking station using the recipe cards.
6. For each student, provide one 5-ounce waxed paper cup that has a small ridge around the bottom.
7. Place the wrapped presents and party hats around the room to set the stage for a party theme. You will use these items at different times throughout the lesson.
8. This lesson can be used as an assessment activity. Observing each student and making notes as to the strategies used to solve the different challenges, the questions that are developed, and the tools which are selected give good indications of student understanding of the basic skills which are applied in the lesson.
9. Journals may be used instead of the activity sheets.
10. This unit is designed to be taught over a period of several days.

Procedure

Introduction
1. Gather the students around and read the book *Birthdays! Celebrating Life Around the World* by Eve B. Feldman. This book has very simple text illustrated with children's artwork. It depicts typical birthday celebrations in 25 different cultures. If this book is not available, use instead a good literature book about birthday celebrations (see *Curriculum Correlation*).
2. Discuss with the students how they celebrate their birthdays.

3. Talk with the students about the presidents and other famous people whose birthdays are celebrated during the winter months.

Part One
Sorting, Graphing, Patterns
1. Give each student a party hat. In their groups of four, ask them to compare hats and have them list all the similarities and differences. Discuss the patterns found on the hats (the colors, etc.). Tell them to record their answers on the recording sheet.
2. Direct the students to decide how to graph these hats. Ask them to decide which categories to use and the graph format.
3. Review with the students how they set up a graph and how to display the hats. Invite them to make their graph on the floor.
4. Ask each student to place his or her party hat in the appropriate space on the graph. Discuss the graph with the students.

Part Two
Inquiry, Comparing, Measuring, Seriation, Vocabulary
1. Use the wrapped present to play a game of *Twenty Questions*. Challenge the students to try to figure out what might be inside. Each question needs to be answered with a yes or no. Teach students to ask questions that will lead them closer to discovering the contents. For example, good discovery questions would be: Is it alive? [no] Do we eat it? [no] Do we wear it? [yes] Do we wear it in our hair? [no] Do we wear it on our hands? [no] Do we wear it on our feet? [yes] Is it shoes? [no] Is it a part of our shoes? [yes] Is it shoelaces?[yes] These questions lead the students to the answer. Questions that are too specific to narrow the choices would be: Is it red? Is it a cake? Is it a dog?
2. Once the students have guessed the contents, allow them to open the box.
3. Direct them to sort the laces in any way they choose and to share their rules for sorting.
4. Tell the students to find two laces that are the same length.
5. Ask them to measure these laces using a measuring tool. Let them choose the unit of measurement to use. Tell them to record the lengths on the recording sheet.
6. Discuss the results.

7. Tell them to line the laces up from the shortest to the longest.

8. Ask the students to measure each lace and record the lengths on the recording sheet.

9. Tell the students to look at the numbers they used to record the lengths of the laces. Elicit from the students how the numbers get larger as the laces get longer.

10. Ask the students to describe their arrangements of laces using positional and ordinal counting vocabulary. For example: Which lace is the longest? [The last one, or the sixth lace, is the longest.] How long is the third lace? How long is the lace between the first and third laces?

11. Instruct the students to choose one lace and find objects around them that are shorter than the lace. ...longer than the lace. Have them record their findings.

12. Direct the students to place one lace in different positions in relation to the box in which they were wrapped. Tell them to describe the position of the lace. For example: The lace is on top of the box. ...inside the box. ...under the box. ...near to the box. ...around the box.

Part Three
Sorting, Data Organization, Thinking Skills

1. Distribute a bag of birthday candles.

2. Direct the students to sort the candles. Tell them to record the rules they used for each category. Challenge them to sort again and again, using different rules each time.

3. Challenge the groups to organize these candles. Ask them to choose an appropriate graph format. Direct them to use the candles or to draw pictures of the candles to organize them into the graph. Remind them, if necessary, to label the graph.

4. Direct the group to write questions to ask the others about the graph, or to write the story the graph tells them about their collection of candles.

5. Discuss the data using these questions.
   - How many candles did your group have?
   - How many red candles, green candles, etc.?
   - How many more red than blue?
   - Which color candle did you have more of in your collection?
   - Describe how you sorted your candles.
   - Tell the story of the graph. What do you know about your collection of candles?

- Can we say that these are all the sizes and colors of candles available to use on cakes? Why do you think that?
- If we all brought in the candles we use on our birthday cakes, do you think we would get the same kind of candles? Explain.
- What kind of candle would you like on your cake?
- How many candles will you have on your cake on your next birthday?

Part Four
Patterns

1. Ask the students to create a pattern with their candles. Tell them to draw a picture of this pattern. Ask them to represent this same pattern using Unifix cubes.

2. Invite the students to bring their Unifix cube representation of their pattern to a floor graph with the rest of the class. Ask them to compare their patterns and to graph them according to the type of patterns. For example: all the A,B,A,B patterns together; all the A,B,C,A,B,C patterns together; all the A,B,B,C patterns together; etc. Discuss how the patterns within a type may appear to be different in color arrangements, but that they are the same according to pattern definitions.

Part Five
Party Geometry

1. Place several objects from the party theme in the middle of the class. For example: party hats, party horns, balloons, and boxes for presents (cube, rectangular solids, and cylinder).

2. Hold up a geometric solid such as a cube. Ask the students to find objects in the collection that resemble the shape of this object. Repeat holding up different solids each time.

3. Direct the students to take an object. Ask them to test it to see if it can roll and how it rolls, if it can stack, etc. Record the results on the recording sheets.

Part Six
Measurement

1. Place the recipe instruction cards at the center or where the students can see them.

2. Direct students at the cooking center to prepare and bake a birthday cake for themselves. Tell the students to follow the directions on the cards. Let them do the measuring and mixing.

3. Get the students to think about what is going to happen to the mixture when it is placed in the electric skillet. Will the cake mixture stay the same? How do the students think it will change? (The students will observe a change in matter caused by heat energy.)

4. When the cakes are baked, discuss the changes

the students can observe. Tell them to record their observations in their journal. (This recipe is an adaptation from the book *Kids Cooking,* see *Curriculum Correlation.*)

5. When everyone has had a chance to bake their cakes, have a discussion with the students about their favorite kind of cake and what kind of icing and decorations they want with their cake. Have the students make a graph with their choices of kind of cake they prefer, kind of icing they like, and the decorations they want on the cake. If there isn't a card that fits their choice, let them draw their own card.

Discussion

1. What are some things you did in this study of birthday celebrations that used numbers? How did you use the numbers?
2. Name some math tools you used and describe how you used them.
3. What are some things you did in which you needed to know how to graph and how to read a graph? Explain.
4. Describe one of the patterns you observed in this activity.
5. What are some other things you could do to use math at a birthday celebration?
6. What changes did you see when your cake was cooked? What were the words you used to explain the changes in your cake?

Extensions

1. Set up a wrapping station for the students to wrap packages and to practice their measuring and estimating skills.
2. At a writing center, ask the students to design party invitations or thank-you cards.

Curriculum Correlation

Carle, Eric. *The Secret Birthday Message.* HarperTrophy. New York. 1972.

Feldman, Eve B. *Birthdays! Celebrating Life Around the World* BridgeWater Books. Glen Ellyn, IL. 1996.

Hutchins, Pat. *Happy Birthday, Sam.* Greenwillow Books. New York. 1991.

Munch, Robert. *Moria's Birthday.* Annick Press, Ltd. New York. 1995.

Young, Dianne. *Kids Cooking.* Dianne Young Publications. Visalia, CA. 1996.

Birthday Hat

1. Draw your hat.

2. Compare your hat to others.

My hat	Other hats

3. Tell about your hat.

My hat is _____

_____ .

What party items are these shapes?

cube	**sphere**
rectangular solid	**cone**
	cylinder

Which ones can roll? _____

_____

Which ones can stack? _____

_____

Which ones can slide? _____

_____

BIRTHDAY CELEBRATIONS

Birthday Measure

1. Find two laces that are the same length.

   The laces are ☐ long.

2. Line up the laces from shortest to longest.

   Measure each lace.

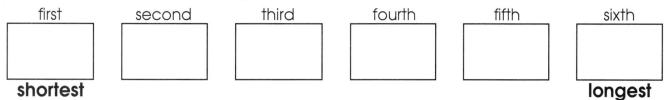

| first | second | third | fourth | fifth | sixth |

shortest   **longest**

3. Find objects:

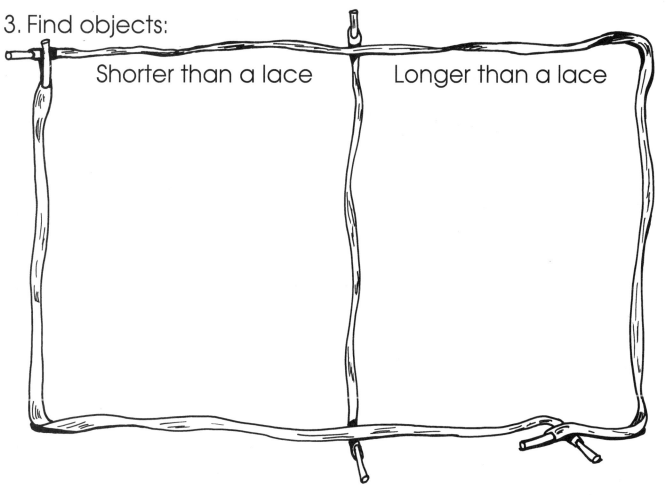

Shorter than a lace   Longer than a lace

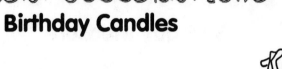

1. Sort candles into groups.

2. Make a graph.

6					
5					
4					
3					
2					
1					

Wash your hands.

1.

Get a cup and a stirrer.

2.

Put three spoons of mix in your cup.

Cake Mix

3.

Add one spoon of water in your cup.

water

4.

Stir well.

5.

Bake at 400° for 15 minutes or until done.

6.

BIRTHDAY CELEBRATIONS

chocolate cake	vanilla cake	strawberry cake
chocolate icing	vanilla icing	strawberry icing
flowers	balloons	cartoon characters
ribbons	plain	candles

114

Count Your Pennies

Topic
Observing

Key Question
What can we learn about pennies by using math and science tools and the process skills?

Focus
The students will qualitatively and quantitatively observe pennies.

Guiding Documents
Project 2061 Benchmark
- *People can often learn about things around them by just observing those things carefully, but sometimes they can learn more by doing something to the things and noting what happens.*

NRC Standards
- *Describing things as accurately as possible is important in science because it enables people to compare their observations with those of others.*
- *Objects have many observable properties including size, weight, shape, color, temperature, and the ability to react with other substances. Those properties can be measured using tools such as rulers, balances, and thermometers.*

NCTM Standards 2000*
- *Understand how to measure using nonstandard and standard units*
- *Sort and classify objects according to their attributes and organize data about the objects*
- *Use tools to measure*

Math
Measurement
    length
    mass
Number sense
Estimating
Counting
Graphing

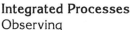

Integrated Processes
Observing
Comparing and contrasting
Collecting and recording data
Interpreting data

Materials
For the class:
    400 pennies (see each station)
    recording journals, one per student
    plastic zipper-type bags
    chart paper for *Station 4*
    class graph (*see Management 3*)

For Station 1: Observe a Penny
    a bag of pennies
    hand lens or microscope

For Station 2: Balance Pennies
    Friendly Bears
    balance
    a bag of 40 pennies

For Station 3: Count Pennies
    a bag of 45 pennies

For Station 4: Pick Up Pennies
    a bag of 100 pennies
    a class graph (See *Management 3*)

For Station 5: Pattern with Pennies
    a bag with 20 pennies

For Station 6: Line Up Pennies
    index cards, 3 x 5 inches
    a bag of 150 pennies

For Station 7: Toss a Penny
    one penny

For Station 8: Put Water on a Penny
    10 pennies
    paper towels
    a cup of water
    eyedroppers

Background Information
    Observation is the process of science that forms the foundation for the other processes. It is important in all content areas that the students become very discerning observers.

    Observation can be qualitative—the use of the senses in noting an object's or a substance's properties, or it can be quantitative—the involvement of a measure or count.

This activity is intended to help build observational skills. The use of the penny is merely the vehicle for doing this. The penny tends to be a very economical manipulative that can be used time and again. Because students tend to have a great deal of curiosity about money, they will find this activity inherently interesting.

Management

1. This activity works best in group of four students to a station.
2. Collect about 400 pennies for use in the eight stations. Refer to *Materials* in order to put the correct number of pennies into the plastic bags. For consistency in mass, it is best to use all pennies minted in or after 1982 for *Station 2*.
3. Prepare the journal pages for each student.
4. Prepare a class graph for *Station 4* on chart paper. There will need to be enough rows for each student's name and enough columns to record the number of pennies students can grab, from 1 to 45.
5. Set up the eight stations. Mount the station directions (journal pages) on pieces of construction paper and place at the corresponding stations. You may want to laminate these for repeated usage.
6. If possible, have cross-aged tutors at each station to facilitate the tasks.

Procedure

1. Read an appropriate story to the students to set the stage for the investigation. (See *Curriculum Correlation* for suggestions.) Discuss what they know about pennies.
2. Ask the students what tools of science and math they could use to observe pennies more closely in order to learn more about them.
3. Tell them they will be completing a variety of investigations at stations to learn more about the penny.
4. Inform the students that they will record their answers on their recording sheets.
5. Take time to describe how students will rotate through the centers. Perhaps all groups will move clockwise, or to the right, to the next station. Assign each group of four students to a station. Describe how you will give them a signal when it is time to go to another station.

Station 1: Observe a Penny With and Without a Hand Lens

1. Have each student choose a penny and look closely at it. In pairs, let children discuss what they see and feel.
2. Encourage students to use hand lenses to make better observations of the details of the penny. Have students draw one side of the penny on their recording sheet.

Station 2: Balance Pennies and Friendly Bears

1. Invite one student in the group to take 20 pennies out of the bag.
2. Ask the other students to estimate and record on their recording sheets the number of Friendly Bears they think it will take to balance the 20 pennies.
3. Have them put the 20 pennies in one pan of the balance. On the other side, have them add Friendly Bears to find out how many it takes to equalize the balance.
4. Direct the students to record this number on their recording sheet.
5. Have the students estimate the number of bears it will take to balance 40 pennies. Give them time to check their estimates.

Station 3: Count Pennies

1. Ask students to look closely at the cup of 45 pennies. Have them estimate and record on their recording sheet the number of pennies in the cup.
2. Invite them to count and record the actual number of pennies in the cup.
3. Next have the students divide the pennies into stacks with ten pennies in each stack. Direct them to put the remaining pennies that were left over in the ones box. Tell them to record this on their recording sheet.

Station 4: Pick up Pennies

1. Ask the students to estimate how many pennies they can pull out of the bowl in one handful. Have them record their estimates on their recording sheet.
2. Direct the students to take turns grabbing a handful of pennies, counting them, and recording their results on the class graph.
3. Have them record their results on their recording sheet.

Station 5: Pattern with Pennies

1. Give the students at this station a bag of 20 pennies.
2. Discuss with the students how they would make a pattern with the pennies. For example: heads, tails, heads, tails, heads; tails, heads, heads, tails, heads, heads, tails.
3. Tell the students to make a pattern with the pennies, then draw their patterns on their recording sheet and tell about it. (Penny stamps can be used to make the patterns.)

Station 6: Line up Pennies

1. Provide a bag of 150 pennies. Give each student a 3 x 5 inch index card.
2. Invite the students to estimate how many pennies they think will fit across the long edge of the index card without going off the end.

3. Have the students use pennies to find out the actual number that will fit. Direct them to record their results.
4. Next have them determine how many pennies will fit on the short side, and around the edge (perimeter). Have them record their results.
5. Ask them how many pennies they think they would need to cover the top or inside of the card. Instruct them to lay their pennies out and record their results.

Station 7: Toss a Penny
1. Discuss the fact that pennies have two sides, heads and tails. Ask the students to guess which would come up the most, heads or tails, if they tossed the penny 10 times.
2. Have students take turns tossing the coin with one person in the group being the recorder.
3. After 10 tosses, have the students record on their recording sheet the number of times the penny landed with its head up and the number of times it landed with its tail up.

Station 8: Put Water on a Penny
1. Ask the students to guess how many drops of water would fit on the head of a penny without spilling over. Have them record their guesses.
2. Direct each student to use an eyedropper to get water from a cup and to carefully count how many drops he or she can put on a penny. Let students try again to see if they get the same results. Tell them to record their actual results.
3. When all the students within the group are finished, have them compare their results using terminology such as greater than, less than, equal to.
4. Ask students to use the paper towels to clean up any spillage and to dry their pennies.

Discussion
1. What things did you observe when you looked at your penny? What did you feel? What things were you able to see when you used the hand lens that you didn't see before? [For example: the statue of Abraham Lincoln sitting in the Lincoln Memorial on the tail side of the penny]
2. What words would you use to describe your penny? [For example: round, shiny, not smooth, bumpy, rimmed, etc.] (Record these words on chart paper.)
3. How many Friendly Bears did it take to balance 20 pennies? ...40 pennies? If you only knew the answer to the number of Friendly Bears needed to balance 20 pennies, how could you estimate the number of Friendly Bears needed to balance 40 pennies? Explain your answer.

4. What was your estimate of how many pennies were in the cup? What was the actual count? What is the difference between your estimate and the actual? If we were to add five more pennies to the cup, how many pennies would there be? If we were to remove three pennies from the cup, how many pennies would there be?
5. Who picked up the most pennies in their handful? Who picked up the least? What is the difference between the most and the least? What is the difference between the most and your results? ...the least and your results?
6. How many pennies fit across the top of the index card? How many pennies fit around the perimeter? What do we mean by the word *perimeter*? How many pennies did it take to cover the index card?
7. Which came up the most often in your group, heads or tails? How can we determine which came up most often in the class?
8. How many drops of water fit on the penny without overflowing? Did everyone get the same answer? Why do you think students came up with different answers? [Some may have used the head side of the penny while others used the tails, some students may have used larger drops than others, some may have held the eyedropper closer to the pennies than others, etc.] What was the fewest number of drops put on the penny? What was the greatest number of drops?

Extensions
1. Have students complete a Venn diagram to compare and contrast a penny and a nickel.
2. Use the descriptive words collected in class to write a class poem about a penny.
3. Have students observe a penny in the bottom of a clear film canister that has been filled with water. Ask them to compare the size of the penny in the film canister to one that is outside the film canister.

Curriculum Correlation
Brisson, Pat. *Benny's Pennies*. Bantam Doubleday Dell Books. New York. 1993.

de Rubertis, Barabara. *Deena's Lucky Penny*. The Kane Press. New York, 1999.

McMillan, Bruce. *Jelly Beans for Sale*. Scholastic, Inc. New York. 1996.

1 Observe a Penny

Look with your 👀.

Look with a 🔍.

Draw one side.

2 Balance Pennies

How many 🧸 will balance pennies?

20 🪙	I think	
	I count	
40 🪙	I think	
	I count	

3 Count Pennies

How many pennies are in the cup ?

I think ☐

I count ☐

Make stacks of 10 pennies.

tens	ones

4 Pick Up Pennies

How many pennies can you hold?

One hand 🖐

I think ☐

I count ☐

Two hands 🖐🖐

I think ☐

I count ☐

5 Pattern with Pennies

Make a pattern with pennies.
Draw and tell about your patterns.

6 Line Up Pennies

How many pennies fit on the card?

long side count = ☐

short side count = ☐

all around count = ☐

inside count = ☐

7 Toss a Penny

Toss a penny 10 times.
Count how it landed.

Head Side Up   Tail Side Up

count: ☐   count: ☐

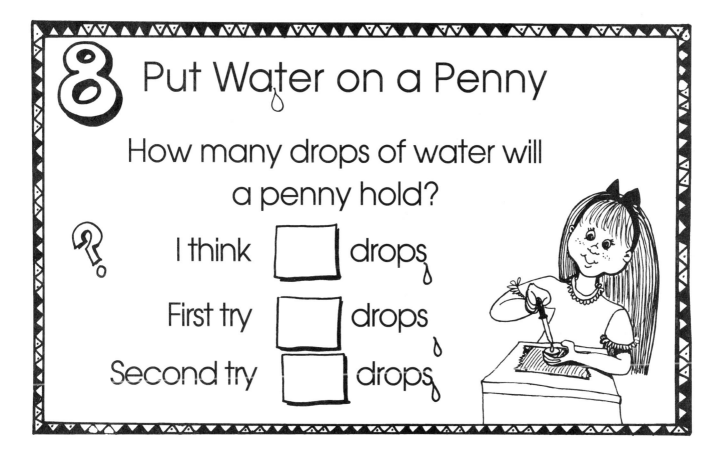

8 Put Water on a Penny

How many drops of water will
a penny hold?

I think ☐ drops

First try ☐ drops

Second try ☐ drops

Valentine Candy Count

Topic
Comparing and sorting

Key Question
What color of candy has the most pieces in the jar?

Focus
Students will discover what color of valentine candy is found most often in a standard bag of valentine candy.

Guiding Documents
Project 2061 Benchmarks
- *It is possible (and often useful) to estimate quantities without knowing them exactly.*
- *Often a person can find out about a group of things by studying just a few of them.*

NCTM Standards 2000*
- *Develop fluency with basic number combinations for addition and subtraction*
- *Apply and adapt a variety of appropriate strategies to solve problems*

Math
Counting
Graphing

Integrated Processes
Observing
Predicting
Comparing and contrasting
Classifying
Gathering and recording data
Interpreting data
Drawing conclusions

Materials
For the class:
    glass or transparent plastic jar (large enough to hold all the hearts)
    12-oz. bag of conversation heart candy
    valentine name tags (with students names written on them)
    prediction graph
    final results graph

For each group:
    plastic cup
    pencils
    crayons (1 crayon for each color of valentine candy)
    sorting/classifying sheets
    student recording sheet

Background Information
Observing, sorting, classifying, and grouping are skills that children need as they are starting their educational years. This activity can be used with various kinds of candy all through the year. Choose any candy that comes in colors for sorting and grouping activities.

Management
1. Prepare the individual valentine name labels with the students' names written on them.
2. Prepare the prediction graph with the colored candy glued on. Have a glue stick available for the students to glue their name labels on the chart.
3. Prepare the final results graph with the crayons nearby for the students to color in their answers. The candies should be in the same order as on the prediction graph.
4. Place all of the valentine candy in a transparent jar that is put in the front of the room so that the students can make their initial predictions.
5. Students will work as a class to predict the number of colors of valentine candy. Then they will make a class graph of their data.
6. They will work in small groups to sort and classify the candies.
7. As soon as the initial predictions have been made and recorded, divide the candy and place it in the plastic cups, one cup for each group of four to six students.

Procedure
Predicting and graphing
1. Place the jar of valentine candy in front of the students so they can see it.
2. Give each student a valentine name label. Tell the students that they will come up one by one to glue their name label on the *Prediction Graph* in the column that is the color they think has the most candies in the jar.

Sorting and classifying by color

1. After each student has had a chance to predict and record on the graph the colors of the candy in the large jar, give each group of students a cup of candies from the jar.
2. Tell the students they will sort and classify the valentine candy by color on their sorting sheet.
3. Instruct the students to record their counts on the recording sheet. Encourage each group to have one student record the count on the *Valentine Candy Count* sheet while the rest of the group counts candies by color.
4. Bring the students back to the large group and tell them that they will put the results of their group findings on the class *Final Results Graph*. Have one student from each group record the results by coloring the graph with a crayon.
5. Tell the students to put all of the candies back in the cup.

Sorting by words

1. Give the students another cup of valentine candies.
2. Instruct them to observe the words on the candies. Inform students that this time they will sort the candies by the number of words on them.
3. Using the *Sorting Sheet* again, tell the students to find how many of their candies have one word on it. ...two words? ...three?
4. Suggest the students could make their own chart to graph the results of sorting by words.
5. Other options: Ask the students how many total letters are in the words on the valentine candies. If you are emphasizing a certain letter that week, have the class find out how many candies have that letter.

Area /Perimeter

1. (Area) Ask the students to estimate how many candy hearts it will take to cover one heart on the *Sorting and Measuring* sheet.
2. Instruct the students to cover one of the hearts with their candies.
3. (Perimeter) Ask the students whether it will take more or less candies to go around the edge of the heart than it did to cover it? Invite them to try it.

Discussion

1. Using the graph, tell us what information we gathered about the candies in the jar?
2. How close was your prediction to the actual results?
3. What color did we find more of than any other?
4. How many candies were there altogether?
5. If we bought a new bag of candies, do you think you would get the same results?
6. What was the total number of candies that you used to cover the heart shape? How did that compare with your prediction?
7. How did the number of candies used to go around the heart compare with the number used to cover the heart shape?
8. What other objects could we use other than candy hearts? Do you think the results would be the same? Explain.

Extension

Use a different kind of candy and repeat the procedure. Compare the results between the two kinds of candy.

Valentine Candy Count

Prediction

Which color will have the most candies?

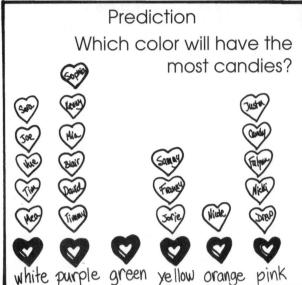

| white | purple | green | yellow | orange | pink |

Students predict which color they think will be found most often by placing their name tag above the appropriate color.

Valentine Candy Count

whites♡
Be mine
Lets go   Time Out

purple ♡
Lost love
Nice try   Nice Try

green♡
Why now?   Sold out
All yours   Plez do

yellow♡
Oh you
Oh baby
All yours

orange♡
U and me
XOXO   Save me

pink♡
What next?
Love me

Students record the sayings by color.

Print four sheets of the graph, overlap and glue to make a large graph. Fill in the numbers.

Graph one color at a time on the final result graph so all students have a chance to color.

Sorting Sheet

Students use for sorting and measuring perimeter and area.

Number of Hearts

72 71 70 69 68 67 66 65 64 63 62 61 60 59 58 57 56 55 54 ← overlap 53 52 51 50 49 48 47 46 45 44 43 42 41 40 39 38 37 ← overlap 36 35 34 33 32 31 30 29 28 27 26 25 24 23 22 21 20 19 18 ← overlap 17 16 15 14 13 12 11 10 9 8 7 6 5 4 3 2 1

| white | purple | green | yellow | orange | pink |

Color of Hearts

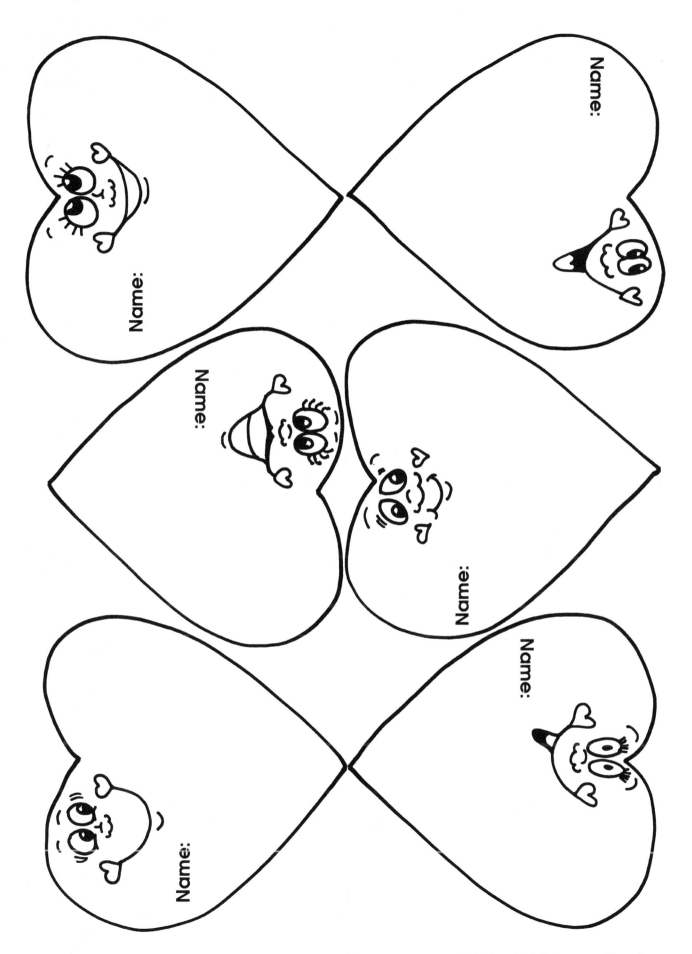

Name:

Name:

Name:

Name:

Name:

Name:

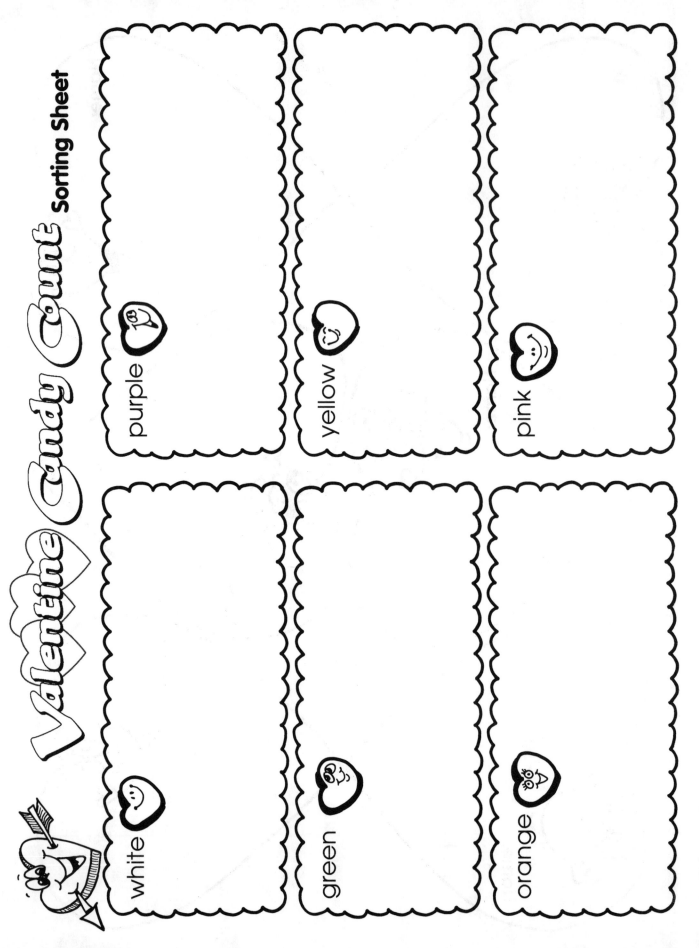

Valentine Candy Count

Sorting Sheet

purple

yellow

pink

white

green

orange

Number of Hearts

white	purple	green	yellow	orange	pink

Colors of Hearts

Valentine Candy Count

Which color has the most candies?

I think the color _____ ♡

will have the most candies.

My group counted

My class counted

white ♡ _____ _____

purple ♡ _____ _____

green ♡ _____ _____

yellow ♡ _____ _____

orange ♡ _____ _____

pink ♡ _____ _____

total ♡ _____ _____

Sweet Heart

Be Mine

The color ♡ _____ was the most in my group.

The color ♡ _____ was the least in my group.

The color ♡ _____ was the most in my class.

The color ♡ _____ was the least in my class.

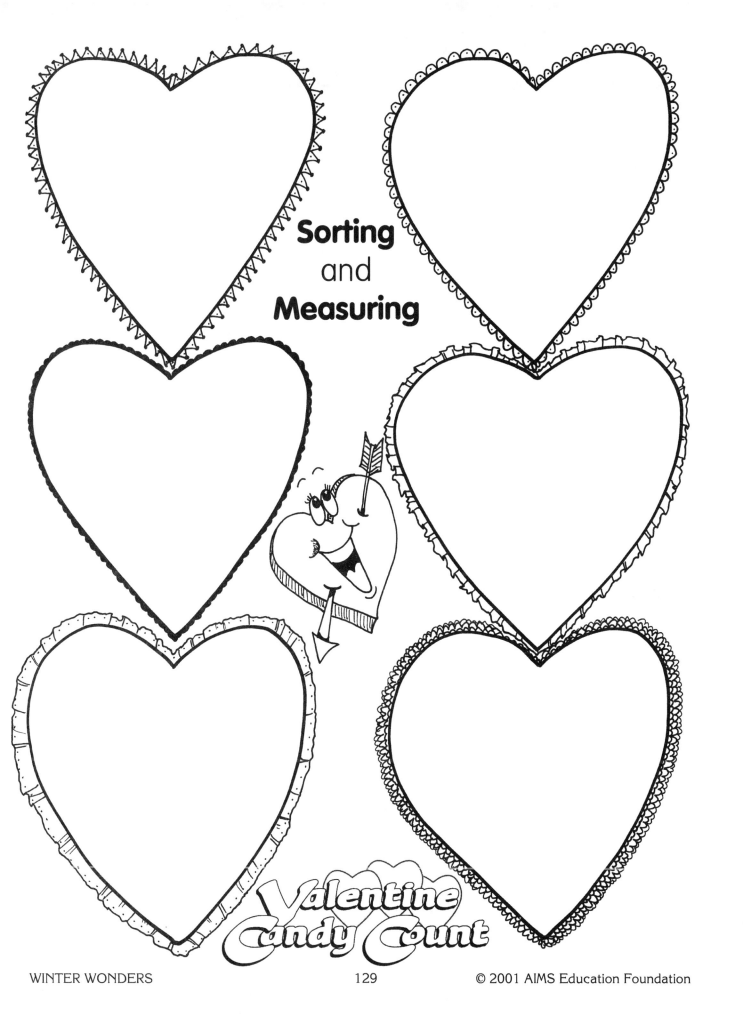

Sorting
and
Measuring

Valentine Candy Count

Heart to Heart

Topic
Sorting valentine cards

Key Question
How many different ways can valentine cards be sorted into groups using various features? (color, number of hearts, words, etc.)

Focus
Students will classify valentine cards according to different attributes using a variety of strategies.

Guiding Documents
Project 2061 Benchmarks
- *Numbers can be used to count things, place them in order, or name them.*
- *Use whole numbers and simple, everyday fractions in ordering, counting, identifying, measuring, and describing things and experiences.*

NRC Standard
- *Objects have many observable properties, including size, weight, shape, color, temperature, and the ability to react with other substances. Those properties can be measured using tools, such as rulers, balances, and thermometers.*

NCTM Standards 2000*
- *Recognize the attributes of length, volume, weight, area, and time*
- *Understand how to measure using nonstandard and standard units*
- *Pose questions and gather data about themselves and their surroundings*
- *Describe parts of the data and the set of data as a whole to determine what the data show*

Math
Measurement
Venn diagram
Sets
Sequencing
Graphing

Integrated Processes
Observing
Classifying
Comparing and contrasting
Collecting and recording data
Interpreting data
Predicting

Materials
Unifix cubes
Valentine cards
Zipper-type plastic bags, quart size (optional)
Chart paper
Yarn, two colors

Background Information
This activity focuses on the development of observational skills. It also permits students to experience various ways of organizing and interpreting information.

Dichotomous classification allows students to observe and classify multiple attributes using a tree diagram for recording the data. The word *dichotomous* indicates that something is divided into two distinguishable groups. In order to build the tree diagram, each branch must have two choices of attributes and only two. There is no allowance for indecision; either the object being classified goes on one branch or it goes on the other. The tree diagram is complete when all objects have been classified on their own branches.

Venn diagrams can show whether objects have individual attributes or multiple attributes (intersecting sets).

It is important that the parts of this activity be done over an extended period of time so that students can process each feature.

Management
1. Have the students return with 10 cards after Valentine's Day. Plan to have extra valentine cards available if students do not bring them from home. You may want to put 10 valentine cards in a plastic bag for each pair of students.
2. These activities can be done over a period of several days. Allow a large block of time for students to explore the attributes of the cards.
3. This activity is divided into several parts. *Part One*—students investigate dichotomous classification. *Part Two*—students utilize the Venn diagram. *Part Three*—students compare and contrast valentine cards. *Part Four*—students order their valentines by length and width (perimeter and area, if appropriate).
4. The student activity page for *Part Three* has predetermined attributes. If these attributes are not satisfactory for your purpose, replace them with others that are suggested by the students.

Procedure
Part One: Dichotomous Classification
1. This part can be a whole class experience. Tell the students to carefully observe their valentine cards. Give them time to discuss and describe

the collection. Have the students describe some of their observations.

2. Place 10 valentine cards in a pile at the top of a sheet of chart paper. Draw a circle around the pile and label the circle *Our Valentine Cards*.

3. Invite the class to choose one property that will sort the pile of valentines into two groups, such as *has words on it*. Move all the cards *with words* into a separate pile, then make another pile of the remaining cards *with no words* on them. Draw a circle around each pile and label which property was used, *words* or *no words*.

4. Ask the students to again look at the cards with words and choose a physical property that will allow them to be divided into two piles (e.g., red and not red). After sorting them into the two piles, draw a circle around each pile and label.

5. Repeat this procedure until all cards are sorted and labeled. (Some ideas are: folded/not folded; animal characters/no animal characters; large/not large.)

6. If developmentally appropriate, groups can classify their own 10 valentine cards in this manner.

Part Two: Venn Diagram
1. Use a collection of 10 valentine cards that have several attributes.

2. Place a ring of yarn on the table. Spread out the valentine cards and allow time for the students to observe them.

3. As a group, invite them to come up with a rule (an attribute) for sorting the valentine cards. Put the correct attribute card inside the circle. Have students sort the 10 cards by putting those with the determined attribute inside the circle.

4. Remove cards and label from the circle and invite the students to choose another rule. Follow the same procedure of selecting an attribute, labeling the interior of the circle, and putting the valentine cards with the determined attribute inside the circle.

5. Repeat this procedure several times.

Part Three: Comparing and Contrasting
1. Make certain students pairs have 10 valentine cards.

2. Provide time for students to discuss and describe the collection before moving on to the classifications.

3. Hold up a couple of valentine cards and have the students share some of their observations. List the words on chart paper. If they have difficulty thinking up words, suggest some that relate to size, color, words, animal figures, number of hearts, etc.

4. Ask each pair of students to select five cards from their set. Direct them to number the cards 1–5. Distribute the *Heart to Heart* recording sheet and instruct the students to put an X in the box that describes each card.

Part Four: Ordering
1. Have groups use a collection of 5–10 valentine cards.

2. Ask students what they think it means to order objects from smallest to largest. (The cards can be ordered by length, width, perimeter, or area.)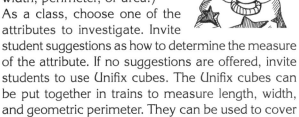

3. As a class, choose one of the attributes to investigate. Invite student suggestions as how to determine the measure of the attribute. If no suggestions are offered, invite students to use Unifix cubes. The Unifix cubes can be put together in trains to measure length, width, and geometric perimeter. They can be used to cover the valentine cards to determine area.

4. Once students have measured their valentine cards and recorded their results, have them order their cards from smallest (shortest, narrowest, least distance around, or least area) to largest (longest, widest, greatest distance around, of greatest area).

Discussion
1. Was there any attribute that all your cards had? If so, what was it?

2. Which valentine card in your collection do you think was the most special? Why do you think it was so special?

3. Who had the longest valentine? What was its length? Who had the shortest valentine? What was its length?

4. What other way could you show the data from your cards? [bar graph]

Extensions
1. Combine valentine cards from several groups and classify and order.

2. Have students draw a card that has a combination of two of the attributes used in their Venn diagram.

3. Choose a student to name three of four attributes and see if the rest of the class can find a valentine card that has all of them.

4. Valentine cards may be used in independent work centers where students can develop their own classification and organizational schemes.

Curriculum Correlation
Bunting, Eve. *The Valentine Bears*. Clarion Books. New York. 1983.

Devlin, Wende and Harry. *Cranberry Valentine*. Aladdin Books. New York. 1991.

Prelutsky, Jack. *It's Valentines Day*. Greenwillow Books. New York. 1983.

Heart to Heart

Put an x in the box that describes each card.

Valentine	Red	Has words	Hearts ♥♥♥	Folded ⬭⬭	People	Animals
♥1						
♥2						
♥3						
♥4						
♥5						

Draw a card.

Heart to Heart Attribute Labels

not folded	no animals	no hearts
folded	animals	hearts
no words	not red	no people
words	red	people

Rows of Bows

Topic
Linear Measurement

Key Question
How does the length of ribbon in a gift wrap bow compare to your height?

Focus
Students will compare the length of ribbon in bows to their heights. They will determine whether the length of riboon is equal to, greater than, or less than their height.

Guiding Documents
Project 2061 Benchmark
• *Tools such as thermometers, magnifiers, rulers, or balances often give more information about things than can be obtained by just observing things without their help.*

NRC Standard
• *Objects have many observable properties, including size, weight, shape, color, temperature, and the ability to react with other substances. Those properties can be measured using tools, such as rulers, balances, and thermometers.*

NCTM Standards 2000*
• *Understand how to measure using nonstandard and standard units*
• *Select an appropriate unit and tool for the attribute being measured*

Math
Measurement
  length
Equalities and inequalities
  greater than, less than, equal to

Integrated Processes
Observing
Recording
Comparing and contrasting
Communicating
Applying

Materials
For each group:
  a collection of gift wrap bows (see *Management 1*)
  Bow Sorting Page (see *Management 2*)

For the class:
  staple remover
  adding machine tape

Background Information
  Using holiday gift wrap bows brings conservation of measurement to a high interest and intriguing level. The bows appear to be so small, yet when opened to the ribbon length, they are quite long compared to the height of a small child.

Management
1. Gather bows in a variety of colors, patterns, and sizes. You may want to ask students to bring in previously used bows from the holidays or their birthdays.
2. Copy one *Bow Sorting Page* for each group of three students.
3. You may want to enlist cross-age tutors to assist with the taking apart of the bows. A staple remover helps; however, some bows can be quite difficult to take apart.

Procedure
Part One
1. Divide the class into groups of three. Distribute a variety of bows to each group.
2. Direct them to sort bows according to size, color, pattern, etc.
3. Discuss the similarities and differences.
4. Distribute a *Bow Sorting Page* to each child. Ask the students to decide which bows belong inside the circle and which bows belong outside the circle. The rule for fitting inside the circle is: *These bows will be at least as tall as me when opened.* Outside the circle would be: *These bows will be shorter than me when opened.*
5. Once the students have completed their sorting, ask each group to select the largest bow and open it.

6. Direct two group members to stretch out the ribbon in the bow and place it alongside the third group member who is lying on the floor. Ask them to determine whether the ribbon's length is greater than, less than, or equal to the group member's height.
7. Using this new information, ask the students to look at their sorting circle. Allow them to change their sorting if they need to.
8. Invite the group to choose another bow and to repeat the procedure.
9. Once they have compared the length of the second ribbon to the height of the group member who is lying down, direct them to compare the lengths of the two ribbons.

Part Two
1. Invite the students to make a real graph using all the bows, by arranging the ribbons from shortest to the longest. Have the students assign a number to each bow.
2. Assist the students in cutting adding machine tape lengths equal to each student's height.
3. Direct the students to use their length of adding machine tape to find a ribbon the same height (equal to), shorter than (less than), and taller than (greater than) they are.
4. Allow time for students to share observations of their data.
5. Invite them to try to fold their length of adding machine tape into a bow and staple together in the middle.
6. Discuss how small the bows of ribbon look compared to the length of the ribbon used in each. Challenge the students to make bows out of the adding machine tape.

Discussion
1. Describe how the ribbon from the bows compared to your height. Was the ribbon from the bows about the same height as you? ...much taller? ...much shorter? ...a little taller?...a little shorter?
2. How did you find out if the ribbons were taller or shorter than you? Describe what you did.
3. How many ribbons were taller than you? ...shorter than you? ...the same height as you?

Extensions
1. Use the leftover ribbon to make a woven art project. Cut 30-cm (12-inch) squares of chicken wire. Wrap heavy duty adhesive tape on all sharp edges as a frame. Cut 30-cm (12 inch) lengths of ribbon and weave each one in and out, in and out, across the square. Continue weaving, changing the color on three rows, forming an A,B,C pattern. Repeat the pattern until the entire square is woven with the colorful ribbon. Trim or tie the edges. Display and enjoy.
2. Use the ribbon at an art center for free exploration.
3. Ask students to search their homes for other objects that may be wrapped or coiled so that the material in them is actually longer than it appears. If possible, have students bring these objects to class to share with others.

* Reprinted with permission from *Principles and Standards for School Mathematics,* 2000 by the National Council of Teachers of Mathematics. All rights reserved.

Going Nuts

Caution: Some students are allergic to nuts!

Topic
Exploring Nuts

Key Question
What can we find out about these nuts?

Focus
Students will compare nuts by their physical characteristics: mass, color, size, and texture.

Guiding Documents
Project 2061 Benchmark
- *People can often learn about things around them by just observing those things carefully, but sometimes they can learn more by doing something to the things and noting what happens.*

NRC Standards
- *Describing things as accurately as possible is important in science because it enables people to compare their observations with those of others.*
- *Objects have many observable properties including size, weight, shape, color, temperature, and the ability to react with other substances.*
- *Those properties can be measured using tools, such as rulers, balances, and thermometers.*

NCTM Standards 2000*
- *Select an appropriate unit and tool for the attribute being measured*
- *Sort and classify objects according to their attributes and organize data about the objects*
- *Represent data using concrete objects, pictures, and graphs*

Math
Graphing
Patterning
Estimating
Counting
Sorting
Measuring

Integrated Processes
Observing
Comparing and contrasting
Collecting and recording data
Organizing
Sorting
Classifying

Materials
For the class:
various unshelled nuts such as walnuts, almonds, pecans, pistachios, hazelnuts, Brazil nuts
nutcracker
metric ruler
Teddy Bear Counters
balance
floor/wall graph
Taste Test graph

For each student:
adding machine tape, for pattern strips
journal
hand lens

Background Material
The name *nut* is usually used for a dry, edible seed that grows in a shell. Botanists describe a nut as a one-seed fruit surrounded by a woody shell. The hazelnut, chestnut, and hickory nut are examples of a true nut. Botanically speaking, most seeds that we label as *nuts* are not true nuts but are called drupes. A drupe is a simple fleshy fruit with a single seed enclosed by a hard shell. The almond, walnut, pecan, and pistachio are drupes. In these nuts, the outer covering dries somewhat and splits at maturity, it is then discarded when the nuts are harvested and sold. It is the endocarp (shell) that we crack to obtain the seed.

Nuts come in all different sizes and shapes. Nuts are usually born singly in a shell. They all have a little plant called an embryo inside with surrounding meat that serves as stored food for the plant. This is what we eat.

In this activity, the students will learn about various nuts through exploration. They will use their senses to observe the characteristics of these nuts and experience using scientific tools.

Management
1. **CAUTION: Some students are allergic to nuts!**
2. It is important for this activity to use at least five different kinds of nuts. The nuts named in the material list are just suggestions; you may use any nut you wish.
3. This activity works best when the students are placed in groups of three or four.

4. Make up a bag of mixed nuts for each group and at least one bag of each kind of nut to be passed from group to group.

5. Multiple copies of the pictures of nuts may be needed for different parts of this activity, or encourage the students to draw their own pictures of the nuts.

6. The students will be using graphs, charts, patterning strips, and a sorting page in this activity.

7. A large floor graph needs to be made for the graphing activity. It will also be used for the bulletin board.

8. Prepare a graph for the *Taste Test* activity.

9. For the patterning section, use the pictures of the nuts and adding machine tape. Make a pattern strip to use as an example of what you wish the students to make.

10. All the nuts used in the activities should be unshelled.

11. Cut the journal pages in half. When all parts of the lesson are completed, assemble the pages in order and staple the left edge.

12. Using the pictures of the nuts, make a pattern card to show the students an example of how they can make their own pattern cards. For example: walnut, pecan, pecan, almond, almond, almond.

Procedure

Sorting Nuts—Use Nut Sort page.

1. Show the students the collection of nuts and ask, "What do you know about these nuts? Have you eaten any of these nuts? Do you like them? Why? Name some foods that you eat that have nuts in them."

2. Provide each group with a bag of assorted nuts.

3. Give each group a copy of the *Nut Sort* recording page.

4. Tell the students to dump the bag of mixed nuts onto the top of their page and sort the nuts into smaller sets of like kinds and put them in the boxes.

Observing Nuts—Use Nut Groups and journal pages 2 and 3.

1. Using the same bags of mixed nuts, discuss the characteristics of the nuts. Help students arrive at a list of properties (size, color, shape, smell, texture, etc.) that they can use to classify them.

2. Allow students time to observe, classify, and talk about the different nuts.

3. Using the *Nut Groups* recording sheets, challenge the students to chart five different nuts. Instruct them to label the top of each column using some of the properties they have discovered about their collection of nuts.

4. Direct the students to place one nut in each box on the left side of the chart. Tell them to put an "X" in each category that describes a property of each nut.

Linear Measure—Use journal page 4.

1. Using the same bag of mixed nuts, explain to the students how they will estimate, then count the number of each kind of nut it takes to cover the line on the *Nut Line Up* journal page.

2. Direct the students to place the nuts on the line, count, and record the actual number of each kind of nut it takes to cover the line.

3. Have each group share their results with the class.

4. Direct the students to place the nuts back in the bag.

Counting a Handful of Nuts—Use journal page 5.

1. Give each group a bag of the same kind of nut. (i.e., one bag with just walnuts, another with hazelnuts, etc.)

2. Tell the students to put their hand in the bag and grab as many nuts as they can. Use the number line on the *Handful of Nuts* and put the nuts on the line in a one to one relationship.

3. Have the students count and record how many nuts they can pick up in one hand.

4. Next have them compare how many they picked up with how many their neighbor picked up.

5. Direct them to exchange the bag of nuts with another group. Ask the students to estimate if they could pick up as many of the different kinds of nuts in one hand from the new bag as they did from the previous bag. Tell them to explain their answer and record the number on their journal page. Have them count a total of three different types of nuts.

Compare Nuts— Use journal page 6.

1. Using a bag of the same kind of nuts, have the students find the mass.

2. Have the students put 10 unshelled nuts of the same kind in one pan of the balance. In the other pan, have them find how many Teddy Bears Counters (or other non-customary unit) it takes to balance the nuts.

3. Tell the students to shell the nuts and record how many Teddy Bear Counters are needed to balance the 10 nuts meats.

4. Have them put the shelled nuts in one side of the balance and the shells in the other to compare the unshelled mass and the shelled mass.

5. Direct the students to record their results on their journal page.

Patterns—Use journal page 7 and Nut Pattern page.

1. Show students the pattern strip you prepared ahead of time. Discuss the pattern.

2. Encourage the students to create a pattern of their own using the pictures of nuts and glue it on the adding machine tape. Give the students time to explain their pattern to the rest of the class.

3. Instruct the students to save the pattern by gluing the adding machine tape on their journal page.

Graphing

1. Combine the nuts of all the groups and have the students place them on the large bar graph on the floor. How many walnuts (almonds, pecans, etc.) are there?
2. Question the students as to which nut there are the most of.
3. Tell the students they have made a real graph, now they will take the nuts off and put the graph up on the bulletin board. Ask how they can show how many nuts they had.
4. Encourage them to draw pictures of the nuts or use the pictures of the nuts to make a pictorial or representational graph showing how many of each nut they had.
5. Challenge the students to take the same nuts and make a different kind of graph such as horizontal bar graph or a pie graph. (See *Graphing and Charting* sheet.)

Classifying

1. Pass around a bag of nuts and instruct the students to take out one nut.
2. Ask the students to gather in groups according to the kinds of nuts they are holding.
3. Tell them to discuss the nuts by observing the size, shape, color, likenesses, and differences. Have them make statements about the nuts that include physical characteristics.
4. Gather the students around a yarn circle on the floor. Place a nut in the circle. Tell the students that this nut is in the family because of the kind of nut. Direct them to place the nuts they are holding in the circle if they belong to this family.
5. Repeat the procedure using various nuts with other attributes, such as color, shape (round, long), or texture.
6. Each time the students place their nut according to a new family, ask them to explain why they placed their nut in that circle.

Taste Test

Check to be sure that the students do not have any allergic reactions to nuts. If there are any allergies, do not do this part.

1. The teacher should use a nutcracker to crack the harder nuts, and allow the students to crack the easier nuts, such as almonds and pistachios.
2. Allow the students to taste each nut. Then discuss their observations of the attributes of the nuts without the shells. What color are they? Are they the same shape as their shells? Do you like the taste of the nuts? Which one do you like best? ...least?
3. Suggest the students use hand lenses to look at the insides of the nuts and shells. Do they look different than the outside? Are the colors the same? Describe them.

4. Tell the students that they will make a class graph of which nut the class likes best by placing a picture of their favorite nut on the graph. (See examples on *Graphing and Charting* page.)

Conclusion—Use journal page 8

1. Have students complete the last journal page, page 8, by describing what they have discovered about nuts.
2. Assemble the pages in order and staple along the left side.

Extensions

1. Make a pattern card by hot gluing the nuts to a cardboard strip, then let the students extend the pattern using real nuts.
2. Have the students make a list of foods that have nuts in them.
3. Plant one of the nuts and see if a plant comes up.
4. Use a hand lens to observe the shell of the nut. Does it look different than it does without the magnification?

Curriculum Correlation

Social Studies

1. This investigation may be coordinated with a unit on Native Americans. Students will learn that Native Americans found their food in their own environment and ate many foods without cooking. They may also discover that the Native Americans used the pollen from the acorn nut as a paint on their faces in times of celebration.
2. Do research in the library or on the Internet to find out where other nuts are grown geographically. How do other nuts grow: on a tree or in a cone (pine nuts).

Bibliography

Llewellyn, Claire. *What's For Lunch? Peanuts.* Children's Press. Chicago. 1998.

Wilmer, Diane. *Nuts About Nuts.* Forest House Pub. Co, Lakeforest, IL. 1990.

Nut Sort

1. Put all the nuts on this bag.
2. Sort the nuts into the boxes.
3. Count and write the number of nuts on the box.

Walnut

_____

Pistachio

_____

Pecan

_____

Brazil Nut

_____

Almond

_____

Hazelnut

_____

Nut Groups

1. Put a different type of nut in each box.
2. Write in traits of the nuts.
3. Put an x in the boxes that are like that nut.

Nuts	Trait	Trait	Trait	Trait	Trait	Trait	Trait

Nut Pattern Page

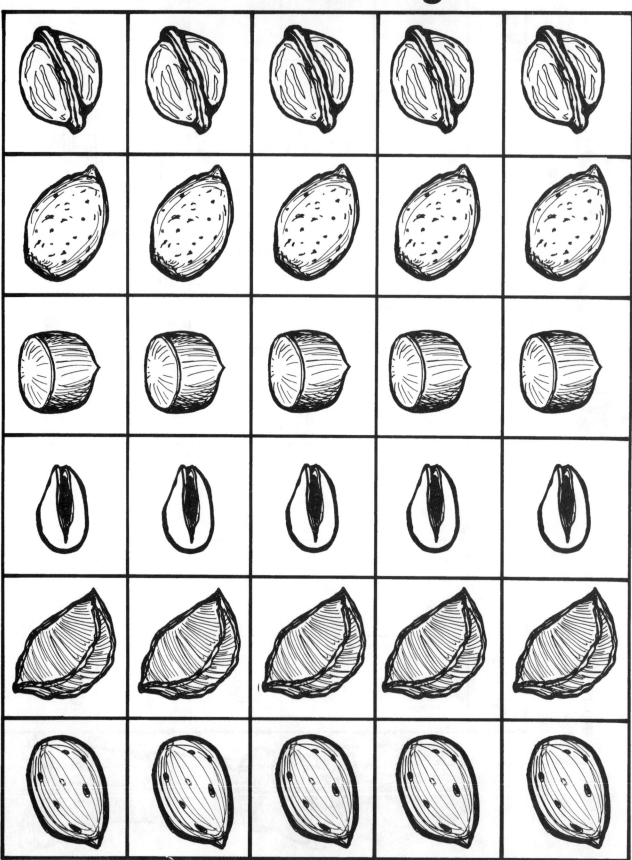

My Journal for
Going Nuts

Scientist:

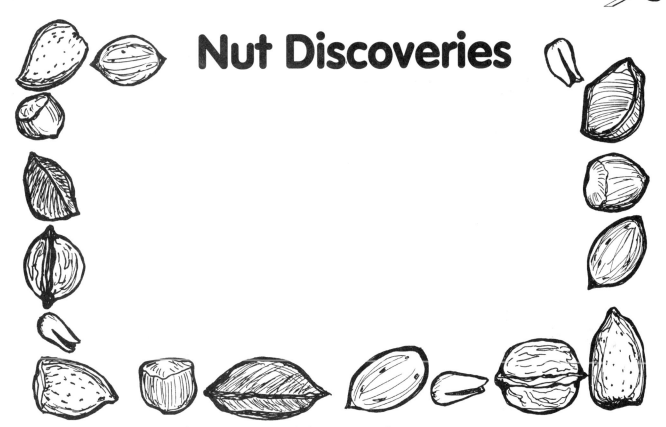

Nut Discoveries

Journal page 8

Observe Nuts

Tell all you can about nuts.

Journal page 2

✂ -

Nut Name	Color	Feel	Shape
Walnut			
Pecan			
Almond			
Pistachio			
Brazil Nut			
Hazelnut			

Journal page 3

144

Nut Line Up

How many nuts does it take to cover the line?

Start   End

?

	I think	I count
Nut 1	_____	_____
Nut 2	_____	_____
Nut 3	_____	_____

Journal page 4

Handful of Nuts

How many nuts can you hold?

1. Grab a handful of nuts.
2. Lay them on the numbered x.
3. Count and record.

X 1   X 2   X 3   X 4   X 5

X 6   X 7   X 8   X 9   X 10

Nut 1: _____   Nut 2: _____   Nut 3: _____

Journal page 5

Compare Nuts

How many bears will balance 10 nuts?

10 _____ nuts with shells: _____ bears

10 _____ nuts without shells: _____ bears

Journal page 6

- ✂

 # Nut Patterns

Make patterns with nuts. Glue patterns here.

Journal page 7

Graphing and Charting

Nut Count

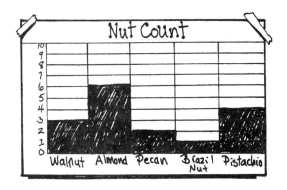

Walnut	Almond	Pecan	Brazil Nut	Pistachio

Our Favorite Nuts

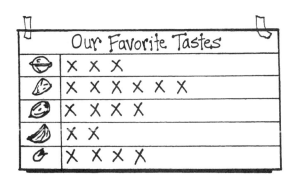

	David			
	Cathie			
	Krystal	James		Frankie
Jeff	Nneka	Carlos		Margie
Barb	Neesha	Kristen	Juan	Christi
Joey	Phou	Ben	Bo	Pao
Walnut	Almond	Pecan	Brazil Nut	Pistachio

Nut Count

Our Favorite Tastes

	X	X	X			
	X	X	X	X	X	X
	X	X	X	X		
	X	X				
	X	X	X	X		

Nut Count

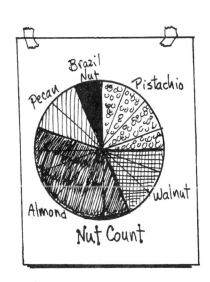

Walk on Logic

Topic
Role playing logic problems

Key Question
How do you solve problems using logic?

Guiding Documents
Project 2061 Benchmark
- *In doing science, it is often helpful to work with a team and to share findings with others. all team members should reach their own individual conclusions, however, about what the findings mean.*

NCTM Standard 2000*
- *Sort and classify objects according to their attributes and organize data about the objects*

Math
Number sense
Logic
Problem solving

Integrate Processes
Observing
Recording data
Drawing conclusions

Materials
For the class:
   two logic matrix floor mats, a 3 X 3 and a 5 x 5
     (see *Management 2*)
   one set of valentines (see *Management 1*)
   one set of school helper necklaces (see *Management 4*)
   string for necklaces

For each student: (optional)
   logic student page
   pictures to represent valentines and school helpers
   student pictures (see *Procedure, Part Two*)

Background Information
As a readiness experience prior to paper-pencil logic, students should experience the logic of problem solving by acting out the situations and discussing the steps. This activity engages the students as the actual characters of the story. There are several different forms of problem solving with logic; this activity introduces students to the use of a matrix.

Please give students multiple experiences (by changing the characters and labels) in the same format as *Valentine's Day* logic problems before you move to *A Day at School.*

Management
1. Duplicate a set of the *Valentine Logic Cards.* The school helper pictures will be hung on strings as necklaces and worn by students in *Part Two* as they role play the various school helpers. You may want students to color the pictures beforehand.
2. Using either a large sheet of butcher paper, chart paper, or an inexpensive plastic tablecloth, construct an enlarged version of the logic matrix student page. The spaces for the characters need to be large enough for students to sit or stand on easily.
3. In *Part One* of this activity, students use logic to determine who sent or received valentines. This part uses a 3 x 3 matrix. *Part Two*, with a 5 x 5 matrix, asks the students to act out the roles to determine which students went to see various school helpers (librarian, nurse, custodian, secretary, and teacher).

Procedure
Part One
1. Using the floor matrix, place three students in the spaces on the left side of the chart. Use the students' names instead of those in the story example. (Stories are at the end of the teacher text.)
2. Place the three valentines you copied in the top spaces across the matrix.
3. Read the clues to *Valentine's Day 1* using the names of the students involved in the role play. Ask the students to move to the appropriate spaces on the matrix. Allow the class to guide the role players to the correct position on the matrix.
4. After the students are positioned, reread the clues to determine if the role players are in the correct spaces.
5. Ask three other students to be the role players. Have them stand on the left side of the matrix. Rearrange the three valentines in the top row of the matrix.
6. Read the clues to *Valentine's Day 2* using the names of the students involved in the role play.

7. Allow the class to guide the role players in determining the correct valentines.
8. Reread the clues after the role players have been positioned to determine if they are in the correct spots.
9. Once students learn to listen to the directions, how to respond, etc., extend the lesson using their own valentines. Model how to design the clues, then turn the lesson over to the students to write more clues.

Discussion
1. How did you know which valentine belonged to ___?
2. What words helped you to know which valentine went to each student?
3. Were there any confusing clues? What were they?

Procedure
Part Two
1. Explain to the students that you are going to read more clues to them and that they are to listen very carefully to determine which school helper each student went to see.
2. Read *A Day at School 1* and ask the students if they can answer the questions. When they find that this is very difficult because there are too many clues to remember, suggest to them that they again act out the parts.
3. Use a 5 x 5 matrix.
4. Distribute the school helper necklaces to five students. Have five students line up on the left side of the matrix and the five students wearing the school helper necklaces across the top of the matrix.
5. Read the clues using the names of the students

involved in the role play who are not wearing helper necklaces.
6. Allow the class to guide the role players. Reread the clues to check the students' positions.
7. Follow steps 1–5 with *A Day at School 2*.
8. Ask the students to write their own stories using the same school helpers and allow others to act out the student-written stories.
9. Once the students grasp how to listen for the important clues, you may want to transfer this experience to the pencil/paper version of the lesson. The students will need to cut out the pictures of the valentines or school helpers and place them across the top of the appropriate matrix. School pictures can be placed along the left side of the matrix to go along with the clues. If your students' school pictures are not available, use the pictures of students that are included with the activity. The children's pictures can then be manipulated into the proper places of the matrix.

Discussion
1. Who did _____ visit? (Ask the same for all students.)
2. Explain how you figured out who went to see which helper.
3. Were there any clues or parts of clues you did not need? Explain.
4. Did you have to read all the clues before you could be sure about all the answers? Explain.

* Reprinted with permission from *Principles and Standards for School Mathematics,* 2000 by the National Council of Teachers of Mathematics. All rights reserved.

Valentine's Day 1

Alexis, Michael, and Amanda all received different valentines.
- Alexis got one that was good to eat.
- Michael's valentine had lace around the edge.
- Amanda's valentine said "Be Mine."

Which valentine goes to each student?

Valentine's Day 2

Alexis, Michael, and Amanda all gave different valentines.
- Amanda's was made of chocolate.
- Michael's was attached to a rose.
- Alexis gave one that was good to eat and said "Be Mine."

Which valentine goes to each student?

A Day at School 1

Jacob, Kristi, Lucy, Jose, and Sarah need to visit different school helpers for different reasons. The school helpers are the librarian, the nurse, the secretary, the custodian, and the teacher.

- Jacob needed to return his library book to the librarian. It was too late, she had already left for a meeting. He needed to find someone who had a key to the library.
- Kristi needed to get a bandage for her skinned knee.
- Sarah arrived late to school so she had to get a late slip.
- Jose got to school early so he checked out two books about soccer.
- Lucy stayed after school for a little extra help with one of her assignments.

Who did each of the students visit?

A Day at School 2

Jacob, Kristi, Lucy, Jose, and Sarah need to visit different school helpers (the librarian, the nurse, the secretary, the custodian, and the teacher) for different reasons.
- Jacob took the class attendance to the office that was next to the principal's.
- Kristi stayed after school to help clean the cafeteria.
- Sarah stayed in at recess to work on a book report.
- Jose got hurt playing baseball.
- Lucy needed to find a book about reptiles.

Who did each of the students visit?

Valentine Logic Cards

Teacher

Valentine Logic Cards

Custodian

Nurse

Librarian

Secretary

Valentine Logic

Valentine Logic

	Custodian	Secretary	Librarian	Nurse	Teacher
Custodian					
Secretary					
Librarian					
Nurse					
Teacher					

Topic
Logical reasoning

Key Question
How can we solve problems using logic?

Focus
Students will pair each person or thing with the appropriate information and eliminate impossible or unlikely alternatives.

Guiding Documents
Project 2061 Benchmark
- *Some aspects of reasoning have fairly rigid rules for what makes sense; other aspects don't. If people have rules that always hold and good information about a particular situation, then logic can help them to figure out what is true about it.*

NRC Standard
- *Think critically and logically to make the relationships between evidence and explanations.*

Math
Logical thinking
Problem solving

Integrated Processes
Observing
Collecting and recording data
Drawing conclusions
Inferring

Materials
For each student:
 student pages
 pencil
 Teddy Bear Counters (see *Management 5*)

Background Information
Logical reasoning is the process by which one works from a problem to a solution. Logic problems give the students experience in considering all available information and then coming to a conclusion. Students need to have many opportunities to make logical guesses about situations while using concrete materials. The students should talk about and act out the situation described. Through discussions and questioning, the students make observations, generalizations, and interpretations.

In these logic sheets, the process of elimination, one strategy of logical reasoning, is especially useful.

By identifying one answer, it is possible to cross out all other options in that row or column, since only one answer for each person is possible.

Management
1. The logic sheets should be discussed with the students prior to their trying them.
2. Encourage the students to work in pairs and to discuss what they are thinking as they work on the problem.
3. Suggest to the students that if they solve the logic problem quickly that they do not spoil the chance of the others to solve the problem on their own by giving them the answers.
4. Starting with *Snow Play,* walk the students through the first logic problem. If the students are successful with the first problem, they will understand the process of the rest of the activities.
5. Beans, math chips, etc. may be used instead of Teddy Bear Counters.

Procedure
1. Distribute the activity page and the Teddy Bear Counters to each group or each student. Instruct the students to place a Teddy Bear Counter on each space on the grid.
2. Lead the class in reading the logic situation.
3. Discuss each clue and the information it provides.
4. Tell students that when it becomes obvious that a space does not contain the right answer, they should remove the Teddy Bear Counter in that space.
5. Have them continue until all persons or objects in the problem are paired with information in such a way that all clues are satisfied. When a student has finished solving the problem, the blocks with correct answers will be the only ones left covered.

Discussion
1. What happens when you find an answer you are sure is correct? [others in the row or column couldn't possibly be correct and are eliminated]
2. Explain how you figured what each person went to do in *Snow Play.*
3. Did you need all of the clues? Explain.
4. Do all your answers agree with all of the clues?

Extensions
1. Suggest to the students that they write a logic problem. Encourage them to work in groups.
2. Use other logic problems in the AIMS book *Primarily Bears.*

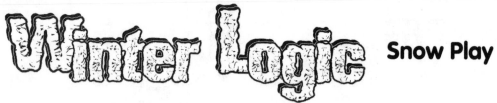 **Snow Play**

The Greene family decided to go play in the snow. Each of the three children wanted to do something different. They could ski, ice skate, or snowboard.

1. Ruth only likes to skate.
2. James does not want to snowboard.
3. Alice likes to skate and snowboard.

James wants to _____.

Ruth wants to _____.

Alice wants to_____.

 **Gifts in Boxes**

1. The gift in the polka-dotted box makes music.

2. The striped box has a gift with fur.

3. The plaid box has a gift with wheels.

4. What gift is in each box?

teddy bear				
ball				
guitar				
skates				

Winter Logic — Home Decorations

1. Joe, Mary, Lucy, and Matt live in a row of homes.

2. Matt does not live in a green house.

3. The girl in the white house has a beautiful Christmas tree.

4. Mary lives next to a blue house with lights on the roof.

5. Joe decorated the outside of his house.

6. Lucy can see reindeer in the yard down the street.

	green	white	blue	yellow
Joe				
Mary				
Lucy				
Matt				

The AIMS Program

AIMS is the acronym for "Activities Integrating Mathematics and Science." Such integration enriches learning and makes it meaningful and holistic. AIMS began as a project of Fresno Pacific University to integrate the study of mathematics and science in grades K-9, but has since expanded to include language arts, social studies, and other disciplines.

AIMS is a continuing program of the non-profit AIMS Education Foundation. It had its inception in a National Science Foundation funded program whose purpose was to explore the effectiveness of integrating mathematics and science. The project directors in cooperation with 80 elementary classroom teachers devoted two years to a thorough field-testing of the results and implications of integration.

The approach met with such positive results that the decision was made to launch a program to create instructional materials incorporating this concept. Despite the fact that thoughtful educators have long recommended an integrative approach, very little appropriate material was available in 1981 when the project began. A series of writing projects have ensued and today the AIMS Education Foundation is committed to continue the creation of new integrated activities on a permanent basis.

The AIMS program is funded through the sale of this developing series of books and proceeds from the Foundation's endowment. All net income from program and products flows into a trust fund administered by the AIMS Education Foundation. Use of these funds is restricted to support of research, development, and publication of new materials. Writers donate all their rights to the Foundation to support its on-going program. No royalties are paid to the writers.

The rationale for integration lies in the fact that science, mathematics, language arts, social studies, etc., are integrally interwoven in the real world from which it follows that they should be similarly treated in the classroom where we are preparing students to live in that world. Teachers who use the AIMS program give enthusiastic endorsement to the effectiveness of this approach.

Science encompasses the art of questioning, investigating, hypothesizing, discovering, and communicating. Mathematics is a language that provides clarity, objectivity, and understanding. The language arts provide us powerful tools of communication. Many of the major contemporary societal issues stem from advancements in science and must be studied in the context of the social sciences. Therefore, it is timely that all of us take seriously a more holistic mode of educating our students. This goal motivates all who are associated with the AIMS Program. We invite you to join us in this effort.

Meaningful integration of knowledge is a major recommendation coming from the nation's professional science and mathematics associations. The American Association for the Advancement of Science in *Science for All Americans* strongly recommends the integration of mathematics, science, and technology. The National Council of Teachers of Mathematics places strong emphasis on applications of mathematics such as are found in science investigations. AIMS is fully aligned with these recommendations.

Extensive field testing of AIMS investigations confirms these beneficial results.

1. Mathematics becomes more meaningful, hence more useful, when it is applied to situations that interest students.
2. The extent to which science is studied and understood is increased, with a significant economy of time, when mathematics and science are integrated.
3. There is improved quality of learning and retention, supporting the thesis that learning which is meaningful and relevant is more effective.
4. Motivation and involvement are increased dramatically as students investigate real-world situations and participate actively in the process. We invite you to become part of this classroom teacher movement by using an integrated approach to learning and sharing any suggestions you may have. The AIMS Program welcomes you!

AIMS Education Foundation Programs

A Day with AIMS®

Intensive one-day workshops are offered to introduce educators to the philosophy and rationale of AIMS. Participants will discuss the methodology of AIMS and the strategies by which AIMS principles may be incorporated into curriculum. Each participant will take part in a variety of hands-on AIMS investigations to gain an understanding of such aspects as the scientific/mathematical content, classroom management, and connections with other curricular areas. *A Day with AIMS®* workshops may be offered anywhere in the United States. Necessary supplies and take-home materials are usually included in the enrollment fee.

A Week with AIMS®

Throughout the nation, AIMS offers many one-week workshops each year, usually in the summer. Each workshop lasts five days and includes at least 30 hours of AIMS hands-on instruction. Participants are grouped according to the grade level(s) in which they are interested. Instructors are members of the AIMS Instructional Leadership Network. Supplies for the activities and a generous supply of take-home materials are included in the enrollment fee. Sites are selected on the basis of applications submitted by educational organizations. If chosen to host a workshop, the host agency agrees to provide specified facilities and cooperate in the promotion of the workshop. The AIMS Education Foundation supplies workshop materials as well as the travel, housing, and meals for instructors.

AIMS One-Week Perspectives Workshops

Each summer, Fresno Pacific University offers AIMS one-week workshops on its campus in Fresno, California. AIMS Program Directors and highly qualified members of the AIMS National Leadership Network serve as instructors.

The AIMS Instructional Leadership Program

This is an AIMS staff-development program seeking to prepare facilitators for leadership roles in science/math education in their home districts or regions. Upon successful completion of the program, trained facilitators may become members of the AIMS Instructional Leadership Network, qualified to conduct AIMS workshops, teach AIMS in-service courses for college credit, and serve as AIMS consultants. Intensive training is provided in mathematics, science, process and thinking skills, workshop management, and other relevant topics.

College Credit and Grants

Those who participate in workshops may often qualify for college credit. If the workshop takes place on the campus of Fresno Pacific University, that institution may grant appropriate credit. If the workshop takes place off-campus, arrangements can sometimes be made for credit to be granted by another institution. In addition, the applicant's home school district is often willing to grant in-service or professional-development credit. Many educators who participate in AIMS workshops are recipients of various types of educational grants, either local or national. Nationally known foundations and funding agencies have long recognized the value of AIMS mathematics and science workshops to educators. The AIMS Education Foundation encourages educators interested in attending or hosting workshops to explore the possibilities suggested above. Although the Foundation strongly supports such interest, it reminds applicants that they have the primary responsibility for fulfilling *current* requirements.

For current information regarding the programs described above, please complete the following:

Information Request

Please send current information on the items checked:

_____ *Basic Information Packet* on AIMS materials   _____ *A Week with AIMS®* workshops
_____ *AIMS Instructional Leadership Program*   _____ Hosting information for *A Day with AIMS®* workshops
_____ *AIMS One-Week Perspectives* workshops   _____ Hosting information for *A Week with AIMS®* workshops

Name _____ Phone _____

Address _____
       Street   City   State   Zip

We invite you to subscribe to *AIMS*®!

Each issue of *AIMS*® contains a variety of material useful to educators at all grade levels. Feature articles of lasting value deal with topics such as mathematical or science concepts, curriculum, assessment, the teaching of process skills, and historical background. Several of the latest AIMS math/science investigations are always included, along with their reproducible activity sheets. As needs direct and space allows, various issues contain news of current developments, such as workshop schedules, activities of the AIMS Instructional Leadership Network, and announcements of upcoming publications.

AIMS® is published monthly, August through May. Subscriptions are on an annual basis only. A subscription entered at any time will begin with the next issue, but will also include the previous issues of that volume. Readers have preferred this arrangement because articles and activities within an annual volume are often interrelated.

Please note that an *AIMS*® subscription automatically includes duplication rights for one school site for all issues included in the subscription. Many schools build cost-effective library resources with their subscriptions.

YES! I am interested in subscribing to *AIMS*®.

Name _____   Home Phone _____

Address _____   City, State, Zip _____

Please send the following volumes (subject to availability):

_____	Volume	VII	(1992-93)	$15.00	_____ Volume XII	(1997-98)	$30.00
_____	Volume	VIII	(1993-94)	$15.00	_____ Volume XIII	(1998-99)	$30.00
_____	Volume	IX	(1994-95)	$15.00	_____ Volume XIV	(1999-00)	$30.00
_____	Volume	X	(1995-96)	$15.00	_____ Volume XV	(2000-01)	$30.00
_____	Volume	XI	(1996-97)	$30.00	_____ Volume XVI	(2001-02)	$30.00

_____**Limited offer: Volumes XVI & XVII (2001-2003) $55.00**
(Note: Prices may change without notice)

Check your method of payment:

❏ Check enclosed in the amount of $ _____

❏ Purchase order attached (Please include the P.O.#, the authorizing signature, and position of the authorizing person.)

❏ Credit Card   ❏ Visa   ❏ MasterCard   Amount $ _____

Card # _____   Expiration Date _____

Signature_____   Today's Date _____

Make checks payable to **AIMS Education Foundation.**
Mail to *AIMS*® Magazine, P.O. Box 8120, Fresno, CA 93747-8120.
Phone (559) 255-4094 or (888) 733-2467 FAX (559) 255-6396
AIMS Homepage: http://www.AIMSedu.org/

AIMS Program Publications

GRADES K-4 SERIES

Bats Incredible!
Brinca de Alegria Hacia la Primavera con las Matemáticas y Ciencias
Cáete de Gusto Hacia el Otoño con la Matemáticas y Ciencias
Cycles of Knowing and Growing
Fall Into Math and Science
Field Detectives
Glide Into Winter With Math and Science
Hardhatting in a Geo-World (Revised Edition, 1996)
Jaw Breakers and Heart Thumpers (Revised Edition, 1995)
Los Cincos Sentidos
Overhead and Underfoot (Revised Edition, 1994)
Patine al Invierno con Matemáticas y Ciencias
Popping With Power (Revised Edition, 1996)
Primariamente Física (Revised Edition, 1994)
Primarily Earth
Primariamente Plantas
Primarily Physics (Revised Edition, 1994)
Primarily Plants
Sense-able Science
Spring Into Math and Science
Under Construction
Winter Wonders

GRADES K-6 SERIES

Budding Botanist
Crazy About Cotton
Critters
El Botanista Principiante
Exploring Environments
Fabulous Fractions
Mostly Magnets
Ositos Nada Más
Primarily Bears
Principalmente Imanes
Water Precious Water

GRADES 5-9 SERIES

Actions with Fractions
Brick Layers
Brick Layers II
Conexiones Eléctricas
Down to Earth
Electrical Connections
Finding Your Bearings (Revised Edition, 1996)
Floaters and Sinkers (Revised Edition, 1995)
From Head to Toe
Fun With Foods
Gravity Rules!
Historical Connections in Mathematics, Volume I
Historical Connections in Mathematics, Volume II
Historical Connections in Mathematics, Volume III
Just for the Fun of It!
Looking at Lines
Machine Shop
Magnificent Microworld Adventures
Math + Science, A Solution
Mutiplication the Algebra Way
Off the Wall Science: A Poster Series Revisited
Our Wonderful World
Out of This World (Revised Edition, 1994)
Paper Square Geometry: The Mathematics of Origami
Pieces and Patterns, A Patchwork in Math and Science
Piezas y Diseños, un Mosaic de Matemáticas y Ciencias
Proportional Reasoning
Puzzle Play
Ray's Reflections
Soap Films and Bubbles
Spatial Visualization
The Sky's the Limit (Revised Edition, 1994)
The Amazing Circle, Volume 1
Through the Eyes of the Explorers:
    Minds-on Math & Mapping
What's Next, Volume 1
What's Next, Volume 2
What's Next, Volume 3

For further information write to:

AIMS Education Foundation • P.O. Box 8120 • Fresno, California 93747-8120
www.AIMSedu.org/ • Fax 559•255•6396

AIMS Duplication Rights Program

AIMS has received many requests from school districts for the purchase of unlimited duplication rights to AIMS materials. In response, the AIMS Education Foundation has formulated the program outlined below. There is a built-in flexibility which, we trust, will provide for those who use AIMS materials extensively to purchase such rights for either individual activities or entire books.

It is the goal of the AIMS Education Foundation to make its materials and programs available at reasonable cost. All income from the sale of publications and duplication rights is used to support AIMS programs; hence, strict adherence to regulations governing duplication is essential. Duplication of AIMS materials beyond limits set by copyright laws and those specified below is strictly forbidden.

Limited Duplication Rights

Any purchaser of an AIMS book may make up to *200 copies* of any activity in that book for use at *one school site*. Beyond that, rights must be purchased according to the appropriate category.

Unlimited Duplication Rights for Single Activities

An individual or school may purchase the right to make an unlimited number of copies of a single activity. The royalty is $5.00 per activity per school site.

Examples: 3 activities x 1 site x $5.00 = $15.00
9 activities x 3 sites x $5.00 = $135.00

Unlimited Duplication Rights for Entire Books

A school or district may purchase the right to make an unlimited number of copies of a single, *specified* book. The royalty is $20.00 per book per school site. This is in addition to the cost of the book.

Examples: 5 books   x 1 site   x $20.00 = $100.00
12 books x 10 sites x $20.00 = $2400.00

Magazine/Newsletter Duplication Rights

Those who purchase *AIMS*® (magazine)/*Newsletter* are hereby granted permission to make up to 200 copies of any portion of it, provided these copies will be used for educational purposes.

Workshop Instructors' Duplication Rights

Workshop instructors may distribute to registered workshop participants a maximum of 100 copies of any article and/or 100 copies of no more than eight activities, provided these six conditions are met:

1. Since all AIMS activities are based upon the *AIMS Model of Mathematics* and the *AIMS Model of Learning*, leaders must include in their presentations an explanation of these two models.
2. Workshop instructors must relate the AIMS activities presented to these basic explanations of the AIMS philosophy of education.
3. The copyright notice must appear on all materials distributed.
4. Instructors must provide information enabling participants to order books and magazines from the Foundation.
5. Instructors must inform participants of their limited duplication rights as outlined below.
6. Only student pages may be duplicated.

Written permission must be obtained for duplication beyond the limits listed above. Additional royalty payments may be required.

Workshop Participants' Rights

Those enrolled in workshops in which AIMS student activity sheets are distributed may duplicate a maximum of 35 copies or enough to use the lessons one time with one class, whichever is less. Beyond that, rights must be purchased according to the appropriate category.

Application for Duplication Rights

The purchasing agency or individual must clearly specify the following:
1. Name, address, and telephone number
2. Titles of the books for Unlimited Duplication Rights contracts
3. Titles of activities for Unlimited Duplication Rights contracts
4. Names and addresses of school sites for which duplication rights are being purchased.

NOTE: Books to be duplicated must be purchased separately and are not included in the contract for Unlimited Duplication Rights.

The requested duplication rights are automatically authorized when proper payment is received, although a *Certificate of Duplication Rights* will be issued when the application is processed.

Address all correspondence to: **Contract Division**
AIMS Education Foundation
P.O. Box 8120
Fresno, CA 93747-8120

www.AIMSedu.org/
Fax 559•255•6396